HAYM SALOMON
SON OF LIBERTY

HAYM SALOMON

SON OF LIBERTY

BY HOWARD FAST

★

★

ILLUSTRATED BY ERIC M. SIMON

Julian Messner, Inc.

NEW YORK

PUBLISHED BY JULIAN MESSNER, INC.
8 WEST 40TH STREET, NEW YORK

PRINTED IN THE UNITED STATES OF AMERICA
BY MONTAUK BOOKBINDING CORPORATION, NEW YORK

FOR
JERRY

An Appreciation of the Artist

ERIC M. SIMON, the illustrator, has lived in three countries. A German liberal, he left his native land when Hitler came to power, lived in England for six years, and came finally to America, his wife's native land. In each of these countries he has a reputation as an artist, and he remembers fondly, in the old days of the German Republic, illustrating Thomas Mann's *Tonio Kröger*.

As a painter he is represented in many Continental museums, or was, until the dictators remade the museums. The tobacco paintings which Mr. Simon has made for well-known tobacco firms, art collectors, and lovers of the divine herb, are classics of picture history.

He has a deep and wonderfully exact knowledge of the eighteenth century, and he put that knowledge into the illustrations for *Haym Salomon*. Each one is the product of careful research, and each is critically accurate. Of particular interest are his two wooden figures, the one being a coffeehouse Moor and the other a tobacco Indian. Both are curious and fine examples of eighteenth-century "tobacco Indian" art.

Whether in a piece of furniture or in a wallpaper, or in the face of a man, Eric M. Simon accurately re-creates the times he portrays. As strong as his belief in America is his desire to know America's history and to make some of it live through his pen and brushes.

HOWARD FAST

HAYM SALOMON
SON OF LIBERTY

PLURIBUS UNUM

CHAPTER ONE

New York

TONIGHT, as he sat down at the dinner table, he frowned and pursed his lips. His wife watched him worriedly. After that, for a while, he seemed lost in thought.

She said, "What is it, dear?"

"Nothing, nothing." He managed to smile.

"Trouble?" she demanded softly.

"Why?" He was a smallish man, with soft brown eyes. He could narrow those eyes, so as to give an appearance of amused innocence. "Why tonight more than any other night?" he inquired. "Today is August fifth. Tomorrow I'm to bid on that order of flour. I was thinking—flour's going up."

"Is it?" She wanted him to talk about his work—the price of things, buying and selling. It was the only safe

3

subject for talk this day. Rachel was proud of Haym's ability to estimate so cleverly the rise and fall of the market—to foresee so well the trends of the day. People already pointed to him, saying, "Haym Salomon—you can be sure he has a shilling or two in his pockets." Yes, Rachel wanted him to keep his mind on his business tonight.

"The British are buying heavily," he mused. "I wonder why? Could it be for a campaign? Two years ago, in '76, they were buying this way—"

"Then let them buy," his wife Rachel snapped.

He stared at her. He seemed to be mildly surprised.

"I'm sorry," she said, "only I'm afraid. I'm always afraid—for you, for myself, for the baby. I feel they're watching us. Haym, won't this horrible war ever be over? Won't there ever be a time when New York will be as it was, years ago. How long can this man Washington go on?"

"How long? As long as some believe in him."

Then he ate his dinner; but slowly, his face clouded, his head bent, as if he were listening for something. As if he were asking himself, "How long? . . ."

How long could he go on, living the life he was living, yet working for the cause he believed in? How long could he go on sheltering American spies and escaped American prisoners in his house? He had a child now; that was something else to think of.

And how long could he whisper tales to the Hessian soldiers who were occupying New York City, make them desert, cause dissension in their ranks? Already the

4

British were suspicious. They had imprisoned him once and released him only because his knowledge of languages was something they needed.

The Hessian soldiers were Germans, simple boys, whose master in Europe had hired them out to the English as paid fighters. And they were good fighters. Only in this case they didn't know exactly what they were fighting for. They liked the Americans more than they did the British, and sometimes a few words whispered into their ears were enough to make them desert.

A few words about freedom. How often he had done it; he, Haym Salomon, whose skill in languages had bought his way out of prison that first time. They needed him as an interpreter, so that the English officers might transmit their commands to the Hessian troops. So an interpreter he became. But far more often than commands, it was a whispered hint into the ear of a Hessian— "Desert— With Washington you could fight for freedom."

The simple Hessian might say, "But they feed me—"

"You've seen the land in America," Salomon would say. "Would you want a farm, broad acres?"

So desertion among the Hessians increased. And the suspicious eye of the authorities was beginning to turn to Haym Salomon.

He paused over his food, staring away at nothing.

"Eat," his wife said.

"Yes—I was thinking I had heard something."

She listened; she shook her head.

"If something were to happen—" he ventured.

5

"What would happen?" Instinctively, she turned toward the room where their child lay sleeping.

"Those men who come here," he said. "You remember, a fortnight ago, two of them slept in the attic. And that time—the wounded man. You never asked me. If I said this man must eat and sleep here, stay hidden, you never asked me."

She stared at her husband. He rose and went around the table, and she smiled up at him.

"I knew," she said.

He put his arm around her. "You see what it will mean if they find out?"

"I think so. Finish your dinner. You know, I'm glad that out of all the men on this earth, I should have married Haym Salomon. I'm proud of him. Six years ago, in 1772, he came to New York, a penniless Polish Jew. And now—behold!"

Salomon sat down. "Behold," he smiled. "In six years he has involved himself in trouble up to here." He touched his neck.

They were almost through with their dinner when they heard the sound of men outside. Haym Salomon stopped eating, held his breath, and listened. And as he listened, his eyes left his wife's face and traveled around the room.

At that time, New York City was a village clustered at the southern tip of Manhattan Island. Almost all of the city lay below Wall Street, and at that time part of the old wall that gave that street its name still remained. The

6

streets were tight little lanes, and on the lanes clustered tight little Dutch houses. It was one of these old Dutch houses that Haym Salomon had bought for himself and his wife. It was the first time he had ever owned a real house, all his own, and he was proud of it, proud of how neat and clean his wife kept it.

But now he looked around the dining room as if he were looking at a thing that was no longer his, that he had known only in the past.

"Perhaps they'll go by," his wife whispered.

The sound was of men marching. The sound came nearer, and then stopped outside the house. A clatter, and then the thud of muskets on the ground.

"No," Haym Salomon said.

He looked at all the warm security and comfort of the room, at the great oaken chest which took almost all of one wall, at the Dutch oven, at the graceful dining-room furniture, made by Angus Loonger in the style of Chippendale, at the wallpaper. He remembered how he had gone with his wife to select the design for the wallpaper, how they had watched it being blocked out in sheets two feet square. He remembered the old East Indian skipper who had sold them the rug.

There was a pounding at the door. A voice cried, "Open —in the name of the King!"

As he rose, Haym Salomon managed to smile at his wife. "Go in to the baby," he said. "Stay with him."

Then he went to the door.

In the darkness outside, he saw the Redcoats lined up

in a file. A sergeant pushed past him into the room. The Redcoats stood stiffly at attention, their hands folded over the muzzles of their muskets.

"You are Haym Salomon, the Jew?" the sergeant demanded.

"I am Haym Salomon."

"You are under arrest."

"And what is the charge?" Haym Salomon asked softly.

"Treason!"

They took him outside. The Redcoats rolled their muskets onto their shoulders. The drummer flicked his sticks. In two files, with the little man between them, they marched through the streets toward the military prison.

A few people stopped to watch, but not many. It was no unusual sight in that August of 1778 in New York to see the British marching a man off to jail.

CHAPTER TWO

SOME people came outside to see what the drumming was about. In those times, the British in New York were anxious to impress people with the strength and dignity of their army. Everything was done with proper ceremony. So when a man was marched off to jail, a drummer paraded in front of him, beating a slow, steady rhythm. And at night a torchbearer waved his light. It made a fine show, the waving, spluttering torch, the drummer, the two files of Redcoats with their high, pointed hats.

But it struck Haym Salomon that few of the people who came out to see what the noise and drumming were about seemed to know him. Old acquaintances and some who had claimed to be friends, but there was no sign of recognition in their faces. People who had done business with him for years looked at him as if they had never seen him before.

"It's safest for them that way," he thought. "Perhaps for me, too." But he realized now, more clearly than before, that everything he had worked for and built in New York was lost to him. Perhaps he would never see his wife again. His baby was a month old. Salomon wondered whether there would be a trial. The baby would grow up without ever having known his father. Would they tell him, the baby, some day, "Your father was hanged for treason"? Or would there be a free country then, so that they could say to him, "Your father was hanged as a patriot"?

He felt a cold chill of despair. Already he was thinking of himself as dead. But why should he give up hope? Even if they condemned him to die, others had escaped from British jails. He himself had sheltered some of those escaped prisoners in his own house.

He asked the sergeant in charge, "Where are you taking me?"

"Ye'll learn, soon enough."

They turned down a side street, and ahead of him he saw that misshapen structure men called "The Provost." Of all English military prisons in New York, this was the most horrible, the most dreaded. Men who entered the Provost hardly ever emerged alive. The warden of the prison, a man by the name of William Cunningham, was little better than a beast. He was the sort of man who hates all men, who lives in a running grudge against the fate that placed him as one of the human race. But Cunningham's especial hate, among other hatreds, was for

10

American patriots. This hatred stemmed for a long time back, from the year 1774, in fact; the year he arrived in America and New York.

At that time, the warden made many uncalled-for and foul attacks upon the Sons of Liberty, an underground organization in New York which was working for American freedom. So one night, certain masked men, members of the Sons, appeared, whisked Cunningham out of his rooms, led him in his nightshirt to the place where the liberty pole stood, and forced him to kneel and kiss it. He never forgot that. It caused some awful change in his dark brain and turned him from half a madman into almost entirely a madman.

And now, Haym Salomon, realizing that he was being led to the Provost Jail, knew that Cunningham would remember him and remember that he, Haym Salomon, had been very close to those same Sons of Liberty.

He said to himself, "Some of them hate Americans and some hate Jews, but Cunningham hates both—" He shivered, and yet it was not cold; it was only August, and in New York, August is never really cold.

The guard detail stopped in front of the prison. The drummer beat a final tattoo. The Redcoats presented arms. The sergeant rapped smartly at the prison door.

The door opened, and a sentry demanded, "Who goes there?"

"The King's men with a prisoner."

"Then enter with the prisoner."

And Haym Salomon was led into the Provost Jail.

11

Cunningham never looked at a prisoner who was brought before him. Cunningham loved his work as warden of the Provost military jail; he loved to see his enemies cringe and crawl before him. He knew all the many ways of breaking down the resistance of a man and putting fear into his heart.

Cunningham knew that if you let a prisoner stand at the door and wait when he was brought in, never looking at him, it would increase his sense of guilt. Cunningham knew that no prisoner was ever certain how much you knew of his innocence or guilt.

So now, when Haym Salomon was brought into the room Cunningham used as an office, the warden did not even glance up. He was writing, and he continued to write for ten minutes after Salomon had entered. And Salomon, staring at the man who had an unmatched reputation for brutality, shifted uneasily from foot to foot.

Finally, still without looking up, Cunningham said, "Your name?"

"Haym Salomon."

"Occupation?"

Salomon hesitated. By occupation, he was a broker, but he also was an interpreter between the English and the Hessian troops. Should he name the first or the last? Should he try for Cunningham's sympathy? But then, they said Cunningham was a man wholly without heart or sympathy.

"Broker," Haym Salomon said.

There was a moment's silence. Then Cunningham cried, pointing with his pen, "You're a dirty Jew liar!"

12

Salomon stood there, silent.

"Well, speak up!" Cunningham roared. "Deny that you're a traitor to the King! Deny that you've been sheltering escaped Americans in your house! Deny that you've been telling the Hessians to desert and claim a fat bounty! Deny that you've been involved in every rotten American plot this city cooked up!"

"I'm a broker," Salomon said softly. "Why have you arrested me? I've done nothing."

"Nothing more than enough to hang you," Cunningham smiled. He was holding a sheet of paper in his hand. "Not the first time you were in jail," he said, studying the paper. "Three years ago, you were in a plot to burn the city."

Salomon shook his head wearily. "This city was not burned by Americans. I proved my innocence, and I was released."

This was in reference to the burning of New York, in 1776, after the battle of Brooklyn Heights. At that time, when Washington and his troops were retreating along the northern end of Manhattan Island, a disastrous fire broke out in the city itself. The British strongly suspected Americans of having set fire to the city, in order to make it uninhabitable for the British, and the Americans just as strongly suspected the British of having burned New York. Who burned the city remained a secret, but the burning itself was always sufficient excuse for the British to jail whom they pleased, merely on suspicion.

"Take him away," Cunningham said. "Put him in Congress Hall and let him stew there for a while. He'll

15

change his mind about many things. And before you go, Jew, remember this: We've had our eye on you—for a long time."

It was one of Cunningham's little jokes that he treated his prisoners according to the position they had occupied in the outside world. Congress Hall was a bare, drafty filthy room on the second floor of the Provost; it was reserved for American officers and more or less distinguished prisoners. It was bare of furnishings of any kind. The men lay side by side on the bare floor or else tried to walk in the little space granted to them.

To this room, Haym Salomon was taken. The soldiers guarding him opened the door, thrust him in, and then slammed the door after him. And to Salomon, it seemed that he had been thrust into a den of lost hopes.

No one moved as he entered. Perhaps twenty men were crowded into the room. They stood against the walls or sprawled on the floor. Most of them wore the vestiges of uniforms, and as Salomon stared at them, he recognized officers of Massachusetts regiments, officers of New York regiments, officers of Pennsylvania regiments. These men were thin, half starved, so weak that some of them could hardly lift their weight from the floor. Their uniforms were in tatters; their beards were long, their hair loose and tangled.

Then one of the officers who lay upon the floor rose and managed to bow. "You're welcome," he smiled, "to our poor hospitality. Introduce yourself."

"Haym Salomon."

16

"The name sounds familiar. But here, you forget names. You forget what you are and what you were."

"I was a broker," Haym Salomon said dully.

"You could have been a king. Cunningham will cut you to his own pattern. When that devil gets through, you won't remember what you were. You'll be—" He waved a hand toward the others.

"But they have to prove a man guilty first! They have to give him a trial—"

A ripple of hollow laughter filled the room.

"Have you ever seen a British court-martial?" a young man in the uniform of a lieutenant of Pennsylvania Militia demanded.

"Beware of the day they give you a trial," another said. "The only time they try a man here is after they've decided to hang him."

They began to ask him for news. Was it true that George Washington was taking the offensive? Or was it true, as it had been rumored, that the American army was no longer in existence?

Was France really in the war, aiding America?

Would Washington ever take New York?

But their interest soon lagged. Their faces were dull, their eyes without hope.

That night, Haym Salomon didn't sleep. He lay upon the cold boards of the floor, awake, listening to the hoarse breathing and coughing of the men about him.

His whole life until this night passed before his eyes. He remembered his boyhood in Poland, and in his mem-

17

ories the people there spoke of only one thing, peace and hope. But there was peace and hope nowhere in the world. He remembered his father and mother, the peaceful family life they lived, and then he remembered, in his young manhood, setting out to travel through almost every country in Europe.

Everywhere he went, he had looked for peace, but there was peace nowhere, only war and rumors of war. Then, years later, he returned to Poland—to find that his country was in the process of being torn apart by Russia, Austria, and Prussia. And Poland, weakened by internal discord, by the spy systems of the three countries, could not resist.

Only here and there young men organized themselves for a desperate effort to keep Poland free. The effort failed. He had to flee Poland, never to return.

He went to Holland, which was known throughout Europe for its religious and personal freedom. But Holland was old and set in its ways, and he wanted something new and large, with promise for the future. He went to England, but he remained there only long enough to learn the language and earn passage money to America.

In all that time, America had become his goal and his dream. America was a whisper that ran through Europe. Everywhere, poor people said:

"There's a land where a man can work and be free."

"There's a place where a Jew has the same rights as a Gentile."

"There's a place where Catholics aren't persecuted."

"There's a place where a man can be free."

18

"There's land there—all the land a man wants, wealth, a chance to be prosperous and raise a family in peace."

It was 1772 when he landed in New York—in a New York that was already struggling to cast off the British rule. He had started in business in a small way, buying and selling; it was what he knew best. But he loved freedom too much to keep aloof from the American cause, which centered in the underground organization called the Sons of Liberty.

Salomon soon became one of the Sons. He became a fast friend of that fiery Scotsman, Alexander Mac-Dougall, and many evenings he spent in hot discussion with young Alexander Hamilton. He began to realize, as they did, that sooner or later war with England must come, that the Colonies must be free.

And then, in 1776, war—and a defeated American army retreating from New York. But Salomon remained in jail, under suspicion of being a partisan of the American cause.

They released him, because they had no evidence against him, and because they needed his knowledge of German to communicate with the Hessians. And Salomon soon realized that here, in New York, he was worth more to the American cause than a hundred men in the field. Here he could keep his finger on the pulse of the British campaign, sow discord among the Hessians, and smuggle information to the American army in the field.

Then he met young Rachel Franks and fell in love with her. They were quietly married. They had one son, born a month ago.

As he lay on the hard floor of the room Cunningham called, in derision, Congress Hall, Haym Salomon wondered whether he would ever again see his wife and child. It was strange that all his struggles, all his hopes, should end this way—in slow death in the Provost Jail.

CHAPTER THREE

THERE began for Haym Salomon a slow passage of time, measured not so much by days as by horror. He had not realized the night before what it meant to be one of twenty odd men confined in a small room. Yet by morning he knew, after a night of lying awake, listening to the groaning, the sighing, and the hoarse breathing.

The windows of the room were shuttered. By morning the air was so foul and thick and heavy that it was almost impossible to breathe. A man near Salomon woke slowly and sluggishly, a tall, bearded man who had once been a captain in a New Jersey regiment. His name was Andrews.

Salomon said to him, "How long can a man live in a place like this?"

21

"Not long. Cunningham sees to that."

"But if we're prisoners of war, can't they treat us like men instead of cattle?"

Andrews smiled bitterly.

Another man said, "He's had twelve hours of it, and he's impatient already. Wait until you've had twelve days, twelve months."

More men were awakening now. They lay almost shoulder to shoulder, so crowded was the room.

"Men have escaped from here," Salomon said. He knew that. He had sheltered escaped prisoners in his own house.

They looked at him curiously. There seemed to be no heart left in them, no will. It was then that he realized that he had to escape, that whatever the British charges against him were, he would never leave that place alive unless he escaped. A sudden fear overcame him, a fear of becoming like the other prisoners in the room. It was worse than fear of death.

Andrews, who was watching him keenly, whispered, "Friend, whatever you're thinking, keep it to yourself. The walls here have ears. Trust nobody."

The door to the room swung open, and outside Salomon saw four Redcoats on guard. Another soldier came in with a large copper kettle of soup and a basketful of pieces of dry, moldy, grayish bread. That was their breakfast, and there was enough perhaps to feed ten men.

The moment the door opened and the man with the soup appeared, the prisoners made a rush for him. They each had some kind of dish to eat from, either a wooden bowl or an old, battered pewter tankard. They each had a wooden or a pewter spoon.

They scooped into the kettle of soup, thrusting each other aside, and they grabbed pieces of the moldy bread. In no time at all the kettle was empty and the bread had disappeared. The men sank down against the walls, bolting their bit of bread and soup.

Salomon hadn't moved when the rush for the food began. Even if he had wanted food so badly as to fight his way through the men for it, he had nothing from which to drink the soup.

So he stood at the back of the room, not moving, watching them and pitying them, hating whatever had made men into this. He was thinking that if ever he got out of this place, he would have no other purpose than to help free America, to make it into a land where men would never be reduced to the level of beasts.

Andrews came back to him. Andrews had done well; he had almost a full bowl of soup and three pieces of bread.

"Here," he said to Salomon. "Have some."

"No, I'm not very hungry."

"Go ahead."

"I'm not hungry," Salomon smiled. "Thank you, though. How long is it since you've had a good meal?"

"I've forgotten."

"Well, I had dinner last night before they arrested me."

Andrews eyed him a moment, then nodded. Salomon watched him gulp down the food.

23

"I know how you feel," Andrews said. "But after you've been here a month, you'll rush for food the same way. Look at this soup—it's more water than anything else. This is what we have, three times a day. When Cunningham goes back to England, he'll be a rich man. He'll have made a fortune out of selling food he should have fed to us. Maybe you think we're beasts, but when a man's starving, it doesn't matter to him what he is."

"I won't be here a month," Haym Salomon said.

Andrews smiled. "You're a Jew, aren't you?" he asked Salomon.

"Yes."

"What made you get mixed up in this rebellion? Oh, you're not the first. I've seen Jews everywhere, in the army, in the supply service, but on our side. What have we ever done for Jews that they should want to die for us?"

"You've given us hope," Salomon said slowly. "There is hope nowhere else in the world but in America."

For Haym Salomon, the hours and days dragged slowly. What he longed for most, word from his wife, word about his newborn child, was impossible. He saw nothing, heard nothing, knew nothing. When he tried to question the guards, they laughed in his face and thrust him back into the room with their bayonet points.

He soon learned that what Andrews had said about the walls having ears was true. No one in the room trusted anyone else. It seemed that Cunningham placed informers among the prisoners, and he needed only the flimsiest excuse, the merest bit of evidence, for a drum-head court-martial and a hanging. The prisoners were afraid to speak, afraid to trust anyone, afraid to ask questions.

Sleeping on the cold board floor without covering of any sort, breathing the foul air, trying to live on the thin soup and the moldy bread, Salomon developed a cough that grew worse as the days passed.

He dreamed of escape. It became an obsession with him, yet the more he planned, the more he realized how impossible escape was. The only exits to the room were through the door or the windows. And the windows were always kept tightly shuttered, barred from the outside. And outside the door, there were always four guards. Even if it were possible to open one of the windows and lower himself somehow to the ground, an informer among the prisoners would have given him away.

Each morning, Andrews would ask him, "Well, how goes it, little Jew?"

And Salomon would manage to smile and say, "I won't be here a month. There's work for me to do outside. I never realized it before as I do now. Somehow, before, I was always watching the revolution. Now I'm a part of it."

Even Andrews caught some of his uncanny hope. "You almost make me believe that it's possible," Andrews said once.

"It is possible."

The end of Salomon's life at Congress Hall came in

less than a week. One morning, the door to the room opened, a sergeant stepped in and cried, "Haym Salomon!"

In the corridor an ominous rattle of drums began.

"The court-martial," Andrews whispered to him.

The prisoners were staring at Salomon as they might stare at a man who was already dead.

"Good-by, little Jew," someone said.

"Tell them all to go to the devil!"

"Tell them for me."

In the short time he was there, they had learned to like the quiet, contemplative little man whose cheerfulness and hope never flagged. But they knew only too well that when one left the Provost Jail for a court-martial, the end of that path was usually death by hanging.

"Have courage," Andrews said.

Salomon tried his best to smile, to wave a hand at them.

The door closed behind Haym Salomon. The prisoners stood there, listening to the ruffle of drums.

"Now why should a Jew get himself hanged as a spy for Washington?" someone said.

CHAPTER FOUR

THE court-martial did not take place in the Provost Jail, but in a flat-faced, red-brick building that faced upon upper New York bay. If it were standing today, you would look through the windows and see Governors Island, the Statue of Liberty, and, beyond, the green hills of Staten Island.

As Haym Salomon entered the room that was to be his place of trial, he passed between four brilliantly garbed soldiers of the Grenadier Guard; their uniforms made colorful splashes of green and yellow and red. To a crackle of drums, they stood stiff and still, without moving. Haym Salomon remembered a set of little toy soldiers he had seen as a child in Poland.

The room was long, and at one time had evidently been a great dining hall. Now, the dining table was set

27

at the far end of the room, extending across it, a heavy board of ancient stained walnut. Four British officers sat behind this table, facing Salomon as he entered, but not looking at him. Provost Cunningham, the military warden, was one of them; the other three, Salomon knew. One of them had been to dinner at his house. Others had accepted gifts from him. But now, as they slowly looked up, there was no sign of recognition in their faces.

A bailiff announced, "The prisoner, Haym Salomon, to be tried for divers acts of treason against His Majesty, King George the Third."

Another officer, a sheaf of papers under his arm, entered and took his place at the end of the table. "Let the defendant come forward," he said.

As Haym Salomon advanced toward the table, it seemed to him that all this was a sort of play, at which he was a spectator. It reminded him of the theater in Warsaw, in London—as if none of this were happening to him.

Yet all this was merely a preamble to the final death sentence. What had happened before, being imprisoned, spending days in the crowded roomful of hopeless men, was a temporary matter that would soon be over. Other men had been imprisoned and had returned to their homes.

But from here there would be no return. He was being tried for treason, and in wartime treason meant death by hanging.

Cunningham was regarding him with a fixed stare of hate. The presiding officer, Major Claud Everle, turned to the advocate, the man with the papers, and said:

"Read the charges against the prisoner, Haym Salomon."

The reading of the charges put forward by the British against Haym Salomon began. The advocate's voice droned on mercilessly, but without too much interest. Indeed, such trials were too common to be more than a bore to the officers who had to preside.

In peacetime, a man's right, English or American, was to be tried by a jury of his peers. In wartime, no such right existed. A military court-martial was not actually a trial. Instead of the prisoner's innocence being disproved by just methods, a number of officers heard the evidence and decided whether or not the man was guilty and what his punishment should be. There was no appeal against the decision.

So, as Haym Salomon heard the charges being read, he knew that he was hearing his death warrant. He tried to be brave, to stand there calmly and face them, but inside he realized that this was the end of all his struggles and battles, that never again would he see his wife or his child or his home.

"A charge," the advocate read, "that Haym Salomon willfully committed treasonable acts against His Majesty's forces in America, that he connived in spying done by American agents, that he sheltered these spies and gave them information. . . .

"A charge," the advocate read, "that the defendant, Haym Salomon, was in secret communication with General George Washington. . . .

"A charge," the advocate read, "that this same Haym

29

Salomon sheltered in his house with his knowledge escaped Continental prisoners. That he aided and abetted these men in making their escape from Manhattan Island. . . .

"A charge," the advocate read, "that this man, Haym Salomon, not content with treason and perfidy, became one of a plot to burn the King's fleet in the harbor of New York. . . ."

Salomon smiled. It was the first he had heard of such a plot. He wondered who had betrayed him. Some of the charges were true, some were false. Should he deny all? Or any? They would hang him anyway.

"A charge," the advocate continued, "that Haym Salomon was guilty of having a part in the burning of New York in 1776. . . ."

Salomon was thinking: It was not only that he had done some of the things they charged him with, but also that he had not done enough. He remembered the name of another American spy who had been tried and condemned here, a man called Nathan Hale.

He remembered that day Nathan Hale had been hanged. He had been there, and he had wept as he heard the young schoolmaster, standing bareheaded in the sunlight, say, "I only regret that I have but one life to lose for my country."

"A charge," the advocate read, "that Haym Salomon, in his capacity as interpreter for the Hessian troops, promoted desertion and sedition. . . ."

And so the charges went on, endlessly. Any one of the charges was enough to hang him; the sum of them bewildered him. Why didn't they have an end of it and condemn him to death?

The officers of the court-martial were hardly listening. One appeared to be dozing. Another read a letter of some sort. Still another stared at the ceiling. Only Provost Cunningham watched Salomon as one might regard a rat in a trap.

The charges were done with, and slowly the officers came out of their trance. One by one, they fixed their eyes on Haym Salomon.

"He seems overly guilty," one remarked.

Another yawned.

Major Everle said, "Does the defendant desire to deny any of the charges?"

The yawning officer closed his eyes languidly.

"Some of the charges are true," Salomon slowly said. "What does it matter whether I deny the others?"

"The lack of proper respect in addressing the Court will not ease your punishment."

"Can they hang me twice?" Salomon wondered. He was tired of their mockery of a trial. A sudden wave of helplessness and hopelessness overcame him.

"Cursed Jews—" Cunningham was muttering.

"Then the defendant admits his guilt," Everle said.

"I admit that I tried to serve my country in whatever way I could. That I didn't serve her as I would have desired is something I can only regret now—"

He wondered whether Nathan Hale had felt as he did now, cold and afraid—sick with the knowledge that they would sentence him to be hanged by the neck until dead.

Haym Salomon sat in the guard room, a small chamber off the long dining room where the officers of the court-martial debated his guilt or innocence.

He had been there for an hour already. Possibly the bored officers had gone out for tea. Maybe they thought it good policy to increase the suffering of a condemned man by leaving him for a time in ignorance of his fate.

A good-natured Hessian stood guard over Salomon. He was a big, lonely boy with blue eyes and a sorrowful face. When he learned that Salomon spoke his language as well as a native, had even been to Hessen, he could scarcely contain himself with delight. He offered Salomon snuff from his treasured leathern box.

"A boy like you could become something with us," Salomon said. "There are Americans north of the city, near New Rochelle. If you would desert and join them—"

The boy froze up and would speak no more. Salomon smiled to himself. They could hang him only once. And his work was far from done.

A while later, the guard came to return him to the court-martial. Haym Salomon stood stiffly and tried to look like a soldier. But he was not a soldier. His work for his country had always been underground. If they hanged him, no one would ever know who Haym Salomon had been or what he had done.

Major Everle cleared his throat, and said, "We, His Majesty's appointed court-martial, find the accused, Haym Salomon, guilty of treasonable and seditious acts against the armies of His Majesty, George the Third.

"Such being the case, with due regard for the state of

war that exists in these rebellious colonies, we do condemn the prisoner to be hanged by the neck until dead.
Let the act be performed tomorrow at the rising of
the sun."

Cunningham smiled. Another officer yawned.

"Remove the prisoner," said Everle.

Salomon shook his head. Even though he had expected it, it did not seem possible that a man should have
to die like a murderer for trying to serve his country in
the way he knew best.

"But your excellencies," he managed to say, "my wife
and child—they know nothing of this. Can't I see them?
Can't I tell them?"

"Take the seditious dog away," Cunningham smiled.

CHAPTER FIVE

IT WAS the first bit of the bread of hope that had been cast to Haym Salomon in a long time; it seemed almost like a sign from Heaven. For late that night, when the guard for his cell was changed, the new guard was the same Hessian boy who had offered him snuff the afternoon before.

Salomon was back in the Provost Jail. Not in Congress Hall this time, but alone in a barred cell in the basement of the building. The night before they were hanged, condemned prisoners were kept in this cell. It was considered best that they should not mingle with the other prisoners after they were sentenced, that the injustice should not be too widely advertised.

There was a narrow wooden bench in the cell, and for hours after he had been thrust into the place, Salomon lay upon this wooden slab, his face in his hands, trying

34

to compose himself for the death that was only a matter of hours. He tried to overcome his fear of being hanged, to reconcile himself to the fact of his never again seeing his wife or child. Again and again he thought that the dawn had arrived. He would leap to the window, stare out at the silent street, try to detect the grayness in the sky that would mean morning and his death. He didn't know why he desired to prolong the hours before dawn, what he had to hope for. Yet he lay in the dark listening to the seconds ticking away on his watch, counting them.

This watch, along with a heavy gold ring, were the two things his jailers had allowed him to keep. His watch was a beautiful thing, turnip shaped, as was the fashion of the day, and made by Lazarus Kurtz, the famous Swiss watchmaker. Again and again, he held it up to the faint light that trickled through the barred opening in the door, watching the hours . . . eleven o'clock, twelve o'clock. . . .

Past midnight, the guard was changed. He was lying on the bench when he heard the new guard approach and talk to the other in the guttural German the Hessians spoke. The voice sounded vaguely familiar, yet such was his misery that he paid no attention to it. Then he heard someone say:

"Hello, my little Jew friend." It was the Hessian boy who had offered him snuff after the trial.

Salomon rose slowly. "Hello," he nodded, attempting to put some sort of cheerfulness into his voice.

"I hear they are going to hang you at dawn," the Hessian said.

35

"Yes—"

"For treason. Lord, what fools you Jews are! I heard you were a rich man. Why weren't you content to be rich without playing with treason?"

"This is my country," Salomon said slowly, as if that should explain everything. He was desperately thinking of how he could turn the presence of the Hessian to his own purpose.

"And Hessen was my country," the boy said. "And I say the Elector of Hessen could rot with the devil before I'd lift a hand to help him."

"Then you don't enjoy fighting for the British?"

"Careful," the Hessian said. "I'll listen to no treasonable talk."

"Is it treason for me to say what's in your mind?"

"How do you know what's in my mind?"

Salomon smiled. "I don't have to be a very wise man to know that you don't like being sold like a cow by your Elector, sent four thousand miles away to fight a free people who have never done you any harm."

"I won't listen to that kind of talk," the Hessian said stubbornly.

"Then don't listen to me when I tell you our commander in chief, General Washington, offers a hundred acres of good land and American citizenship to any Hessian who deserts to the American ranks. Think of it, man!"

The Hessian's eyes grew round. "A hundred acres," he said slowly. "In Hessen, a count does not own more than that."

36

"And a hundred acres more as soon as you can plow them."

The Hessian shook his head. "You're lying."

"I'm not lying. It doesn't matter to me. I'm going to die in the morning. But I hate to see a boy like you fight against men who want only to be free and to live in peace."

"You know what they do if they capture a Hessian who deserts."

"It's no worse than being killed fighting for something you don't believe. I'd help you. I have a gold ring here that's worth fifty Dutch dollars and a Swiss watch that's worth three hundred more. You were good to me; you can have them."

The Hessian shook his head. "That's too much. I can do nothing for you."

"Three hundred and fifty dollars is a lot of money," Salomon said. "Perhaps you have a father or a mother in the old country. Perhaps you would want to bring them over here—"

"I have an old mother," the Hessian said. "If I could do something to repay you?"

Then Haym Salomon staked everything on one chance. "You can—desert tonight. Go north and contact the Americans. Only leave the door of this cell open. I'll give you an hour to get clear of the city, so that if you're captured or turned back I'll still be here and you won't be blamed for my escape. If nothing happens in an hour, I'll try to get away."

The Hessian shook his head.

37

Salomon gave him the watch and the ring. "Become an American tonight," Salomon said softly.

The boy stared at the watch and the ring in his hand. There was nothing more Salomon could do or say. He went back to the wooden bench and sat down.

Even at this distance from the door of his cell, he heard the watch ticking. Then the sound was muffled; then there was the grating noise of a key turning in a lock. Then quick footsteps.

Then silence.

Haym Salomon didn't move. He sat on the bench, scarcely daring to breath, scarcely daring to hope. He listened to the grim silence of the prison all around him. He listened for an outcry, for the sharp sound of a sentry halting the deserting Hessian.

A rat ran across the floor. Upstairs some of the prisoners stirred, and the walls and floors of the old prison creaked.

He tried to count the seconds, the minutes. He tried to mark off on his fingers each time five minutes had passed. Again and again he almost started to his feet, believing that an hour had passed. Again and again he sank back, sighing.

He bit his lips until he tasted the blood in his mouth. The nails of his clenched hands broke through his skin.

"Time at last," he decided.

His hand trembled as he tried the door. The knob turned, rasped. The whole door needed oiling. It seemed to shriek aloud as he drew it open.

38

Then he was in the corridor. A single candle, set in the mouth of a brown jug, burned there. It threw a flickering, ghostly flame.

He tried to remember the direction of the outer door, and then he moved slowly in the opposite direction. There would be two sentries outside the door, and he must find another way out of the building. He heard a voice ahead of him, and he groped in the dark desperately. His hand found a door, and he opened it and slipped through. Wooden stairs led down. The smell of old wood and moldy potatoes filled his nostrils. He knew he was in the store cellar of the building, the place where Cunningham kept the rotten food he fed the prisoners.

In pitch blackness, he felt his way across the cellar. His head hit something. He reached up and felt a pair of cellar doors. Slowly he lifted one of them and felt the cool, fresh air of night across his cheeks.

He climbed up slowly and then pressed back against the wall of the house when he stood in the street. A sentry passed not five feet from him, but the sentry stared straight ahead. As soon as the sentry had rounded the corner of the building, Haym Salomon dashed across the street, tumbled into an alleyway, pulled himself over a fence, ripping his shirt, and then tumbled silently into some Dutch housewife's vegetable garden. He lay there panting.

He was free.

CHAPTER SIX

WITHOUT moving, Haym Salomon lay in the garden, praying that this family owned no dog. He listened for some outcry from the prison that would denote knowledge of his escape, and when none came, he dared to move.

Cabbage took shape unded his hand and carrot top brushed his face. He rolled over and came slowly to his feet. He crossed the garden, went out a gate at the farther end, and slipped along a dark, twisting alley that he knew. At the other end, he stopped. The watch was coming up the street, calling sleepily:

"Three o'clock—and all's well."

Salomon crossed the street, lost himself again in the darkness between a stable and an alleyway. Over his shoulder, he could see a faint glimmer from the bay, lamps hung high in the masts of ships that floated at anchor. A horse in the stable champed restlessly in its sleep.

He was on the street again, and now he ran northward, trying to smother his hoarse coughs. Presently he was on the very street where his own house stood. He crouched behind a fence and stared for a moment at the familiar outlines. Somewhere in that house were his wife and child. If only he dared go into them, see them both once more. If only to hold his wife in his arms a moment before he left her for God only knew how long, if only to touch his child's face. Did he dare? Wasn't it better to leave this way?

Yet she must have heard that he had been condemned to death. If he could spare her the few hours of torture before she was informed of his escape—

He had almost made up his mind to enter his house when he heard the stamp of marching feet. A guard detail was coming up the street. Did they know of his escape already? Would they stop at his house?

They did. Haym Salomon waited to see no more. From now on, he was a hunted man, and his ways must be the ways of the hunted beast. Somewhere to the north of him (in what is now Westchester County) were American forces. Until he reached them, there would be safety nowhere. The chase would be like a fox hunt, with him playing the part of the fox, and all the time he would be imprisoned by the waters that circled Manhattan Island.

He heard the sound of a musket being pounded on the door of his home, and he slipped along the fence. Only once he looked back, and there was a brief picture of his wife, standing in the open doorway, holding a candle. For months afterward, he remembered that picture of her.

He cut back through an alleyway, ran along a street, and then twisted north. He was on Beaver Street, and he followed it until he reached what is now the intersection with Exchange Place. He ran down Exchange Place, heard the footsteps of an approaching guard, and switched north to Wall Street. So far, he had managed to remain unseen. Under part of what had once been the old wall, he stopped, panting.

Then he passed through the wall and went on. Here, even at that time, were still streets, but the houses took on a country air, and occasionally there was a little farm that the city had overtaken in its northward march.

The best thoroughfare north through Manhattan Island, at that time, followed the path Broadway takes today. But he knew that the first place they would cover would be this road. Instead, he worked eastward, and soon he had reached the northern limits of the city. Here were only country homes and farms, and here, for some reason, he felt more secure.

He was very tired now. The time he had spent in prison had weakened him. And soon it would be dawn. In the daytime, they could run him down very easily. As he stumbled along in the darkness, he tried to find a place where he could hide and sleep.

A dog barked, and he remembered that the British used hounds to hunt escaped prisoners. He came to a brook and walked through it, hoping that such a device would throw them off the scent. He avoided all main roads, using the little country lanes that twisted back and forth all through Manhattan.

He was so tired now that he stumbled along half asleep. He hardly cared now where he slept, so long as he slept. And as the first elation of escape wore off, weariness took its place.

He came to a hay field, where the stacks were piled up like ghostly tents in the night. Already the gray of dawn was breaking in the east. He crawled through the fence, went to the nearest haystack, and burrowed deep into it. And almost immediately he was asleep.

When he awoke, the sun was already setting, and he realized that he had more than slept the clock around. He was stiff and hungry, but he waited until it was dark before he crept out of his hiding place in the haystack. Meanwhile, he watched the farmer driving in his cows from pasture.

With darkness, he started out again, making his way north. He found some apple trees, and he filled his shirt with apples and a few ears of sweet corn that had been overlooked in the harvesting. As he walked along, he munched on the apples and corn. At a brook, he stopped and drank his fill.

Once he was passed by a wagon full of laughing boys and girls. He shrank into the bushes, and for a long time after they had passed, he heard their laughter echoing. He wished, for a moment, that he could be like them, with nothing to think of and nothing to fear.

43

He missed his watch. It was hard to try to gauge time. Also, in the dark, he could not move as fast as he would have liked to. At that time, the city was concentrated at the southern tip of Manhattan. Greenwich Village, which is a neighborhood extending today from Fourth Street to Tenth Street and from Fifth Avenue to Seventh Avenue, was then a little country village, a suburb of New York. Dutch farms sprawled beneath Twenty-third Street, and from there up to where Columbus Circle is today the farms grew less frequent. Manhattan was an island of wooded hills, and there were still great forests, stretching in some places almost without a break from the East River to the Hudson. Here and there were country homes, like the Murray place, which was not far from where Grand Central Station is now. Central Park and the land near it was a wooded wilderness; Morningside Heights a beautiful hill, still clothed with forest. Uptown, through Washington Heights and Inwood, at the northern tip of the island, the farms were scattered, almost lost in the forest. Deer roamed through that section, and it was not unusual to find a fat black bear waddling along one of the paths that later became Broadway or Amsterdam Avenue.

So Haym Salomon, keeping away from the main roads, often had to force his way through tangled underbrush or plod along low-lying swampy marsh. During the years he had lived in New York, he had often gone on daylight trips up through Manhattan, but in the night landmarks changed. It was only when he came to the top of some cleared knoll and was able to see the gleam of the

44

river on one side or the other that he had a chance to guess where he was. And even then, he could not be certain; he could only hope that his path led north toward Spuyten Duyvil.

Once he almost blundered straight into the arms of a British patrol that apparently was searching for him. He had crossed a field in the moonlight and had come on a little lane that wandered north and seemed isolated enough to be fairly safe. He started along it, and then the thunder of hoofs sent him clambering over a stone wall. Through a crevice in the rocks, he saw a body of dragoons dash past. He lay there until the sound of their hoofs had faded in the night.

By midnight, he was on Morningside Heights, with all the moon-swept glory of Harlem and the Bronx beneath him. The majesty of that sea of silvery black, broken only here and there by the cleared space of a farm, quieted his soul and gave him new faith in what he planned to do. This was his land. Here he would struggle and die, and this would be the home of his children.

He was clambering down into the valley that separates Morningside Heights from Washington Heights, when he heard, from far off, the baying of hounds. Apparently the British had picked up his trail and were following him now in the night.

He began to run, stumbling, falling, but exerting all his strength to leave that dread noise behind him. He knew that unless he found another stream in which to lose the scent, the hounds would sooner or later find him.

45

He reached the bottom of the hill gasping for breath, crossed the pastures of a farm, and saw in front of him a muddy trace of water. He followed it for almost a hundred yards and then climbed a rocky slope toward Washington Heights. The dogs could not follow him there. He walked more slowly as he reached the wooded ridges of the Heights. Perhaps they would presume that he had taken the easier path down into the valley.

He trudged on. A rim of clouds covered the face of the moon, and that gave him added confidence. Soon he was within a mile of Fort Washington, which had been lost to the British in 1776 through the treachery of Adjutant-General William Demont. He remembered his despair when the awful news of that defeat was brought down to the city. Since then many battles had been fought, and now, though the end of the war was not yet in sight, there was hope for the American cause.

In those times there stood, not far from 181st Street and Broadway today, a tavern and exchange stable for post horses. Haym Salomon approached it slowly and cautiously, and it was well that he did so, for almost a full troop of dragoons were standing in front of it, holding their horses, all saddled and ready to mount and ride. He crouched in the brush and heard their officers giving them orders to bar all roads and paths leading down from the ridge into the valley of Inwood.

"The Jew should be here soon," the officer said.

And for the first time in many days, Haym Salomon smiled with real pleasure. His fear had left him, and now that they were so close to him, he felt more confident than ever before that he would escape.

He moved away cautiously, yet not so quietly but that the brush rustled. Some of the dragoons turned in his direction. And then, as if in answer to their unspoken question, a rabbit leaped from the brush and scampered past their feet. They smiled.

Salomon moved westward. What he had seen seemed to give him new strength as he scrambled through the brush and down the cliff to the Hudson. Here he made his way northward in the forest, around the jutting hill that gave Fort Washington its commanding position. He struck the old cart road leading past the place where a little village of Indians still existed, in what is today known as Inwood Hill Park. Then he turned eastward, past the Dykeman House and down to Spuyten Duyvil Creek.

He was very tired when he reached the bank of the stream that marked the northern end of Manhattan Island, but also elated and thrilled with the prospect of escape.

Today, Spuyten Duyvil is an imposing ship canal through which tugs and even small ocean-going freighters can pass, but then it was a small stream, shallow enough in places to wade across.

For a while, Salomon rested on the bank. Then he stepped into the water and started to cross. In places the water was so deep that he sank to his armpits, but he continued on without stopping. He was almost at the farther bank when he heard hoofbeats on the Manhattan shore.

As he splashed through the last few feet of water, a volley of musketry broke the night behind him. But the bullets fell short, and he heard horses splashing into the water.

The prospect of being captured now, when he had almost won his way to freedom, lent him new strength. He ran on desperately, but he was too weakened to go far. He found himself on a road, ran along it, and saw a house loom through the night.

The hoofbeats were coming hard behind him.

He pounded on the door until a light appeared. He was half dead with weariness, soaking wet. He had to take this chance.

A man in a nightshirt opened the door. "Who's there?" he demanded. He had a musket in his hand, and he thrust the muzzle into Salomon's stomach.

"An American. I escaped from a British prison. For the love of God, let me in! I'm half dead, and they're right behind me."

"How do I know—" The man now saw Salomon in the light of his lantern. He whistled, then appeared to notice for the first time the hoofbeats. "In here," he said.

He barred the door. Salomon stood in the hallway, shivering. A woman, wrapped in a robe, came down the stairs, and said:

"What is it, dear?"

"Tell you later. You've seen nothing." He opened the door of a tiny cupboard under the stairs and thrust Salomon in. Then the door closed, and Haym Salomon stood

48

in darkness, wondering whether this was the end of everything.

He heard the British pounding on the door, heard the man's sleepy voice telling them, "No—I haven't seen anyone—no one. A fine business, to wake a man at this hour of the night. No."

Salomon heard the door closing, then silence. Then the door of his hiding place opened.

"You can come out now," the man said. "I think you're safe."

CHAPTER SEVEN

AFTERWARD, that night was like a dream for Haym Salomon. Hot food, a pot of steaming coffee, and then a deep feather bed. He was too weary to ask questions or to answer them, and evidently the man and his wife understood that.

It was midafternoon when he awoke; dawn had been breaking when he fell asleep. He found clean stockings, a pair of old but serviceable breeches, and a clean shirt laid out for him. They were a welcome change after his own tattered, mud-caked garments.

A twelve-year-old boy came into the room as he finished dressing. The boy stood there silently, regarding him with deep and respectful interest. Then he led Haym Salomon downstairs.

The woman was standing in front of a Dutch oven,

50

stirring a pot of steaming, savory stew. She smiled as Salomon appeared.

"They must have wanted you a great deal," she said. "They've been combing the neighborhood all morning."

"I can never thank you enough for what you've done for me. I don't know why you've done it. If they had found me here, things would have gone hard with you."

"You're an American," the woman said, as if that should explain everything. She dipped up a bowl of the stew and set it on the table with milk and bread. "We know what it is to be in one of their prisons. We have a boy of our own—with Washington. Now eat. You'll need all your strength."

"At least, let me know the name of my benefactor."

"Vanhelb. My husband is Jan Vanhelb."

"You're Dutch," Salomon nodded. "I thought so. My name is Haym Salomon."

The woman looked at him queerly. "Where are you from? You speak strangely."

"From Poland. I'm a Jew."

The boy stared, his eyes almost popping. It was the first time he had ever seen a Jew. Somehow he had expected them to be different, perhaps with horns even. But all he saw was a small, brown-eyed, mild-mannered little man.

"And why—" the woman began.

"And why they put me in prison? Because I tried to help my country in whatever small way I could. I didn't do enough, not one quarter as much as other men have done. But it was enough for them to sentence me to be hanged. I escaped—"

51

"Finish eating," Mrs. Vanhelb said. "We will talk about those things later."

It was dusk when Jan Vanhelb came into the house. He greeted Salomon heartily and then sat down with the family for supper. He was silent all the while they ate, listening to his wife's comments and sometimes glancing shrewdly at Haym Salomon. When they had finished, he leaned back and said:

"They want you pretty badly, Salomon, but this evening they had about given up the search. They're convinced you've escaped. Because you're a Jew, they'd like more than ever to hang you. I heard you left a home and a business and a wife and child back there in the city. That's hard, but war is always hard. Later, I'll try to get word to her."

Salomon nodded his thanks. He found it difficult to speak.

"Have you any plans?" Vanhelb asked.

"Only to escape," Salomon said. "When you're going to be hanged, it's enough to keep the rope away from your neck. There are other things I thought of. I want to help this revolution. I wouldn't be much of a soldier, and besides Washington has all the men he needs now. But there are other ways in which to serve, there must be. I've thought of Philadelphia. It's the heart of the nation right now. If something great is to come from the revolution, it will come from Philadelphia as well as from the army in the field."

"That may or may not be," Vanhelb said. "Anyway,

you have to get out of here as soon as we can manage it, tonight perhaps. It won't be long before they come back and search my house. Now I hear there are American troops at Dobbs Ferry. That's only a few hours' ride up the river. The main thing is to get through to them. Can you ride?"

Salomon nodded.

"Then we leave as soon as it is dark."

Ever since 1776, when Washington had been defeated in the Battle of Long Island and had retreated through Manhattan north to the Bronx, the British had held New York City. But while they held the city itself, then a little village clustered at the southern tip of Manhattan, the country surrounding the city was a sort of no man's land. Daring American forces hung onto the flanks of the British, and American cavalry raided as far south as where Kingsbridge Road is today. The British patrolled the Bronx shore of Spuyten Duyvil, where Salomon had found shelter, but their patrols hardly ever ventured even as far north as Van Cortlandt Park. They were always in fear of being cut off by American raiders. So between where the city of Yonkers starts today and Dobbs Ferry there was a fifteen-mile stretch of wild and lawless land, a place where neither the Americans nor the British ruled, where farmers barred their windows at night and kept their muskets loaded.

It was not soldiers that were to be feared in this section, but the robbers and highwaymen who had made it their own special province.

53

Lawless characters from every part of the state had drifted into this section. They preyed upon honest farmers and they preyed upon the caravans that brought food to the British. They waylaid travelers and left them either stripped clean or dead.

So Vanhelb loaded his musket carefully and gave a long pistol to Salomon. Then he saddled two horses, and with nightfall the two of them rode off to the north. Vanhelb was a grain dealer. His mind was a map of all the roads and lanes of Westchester. At first they rode slowly, turning eastward and following a lane that took almost the course Baily Avenue takes today. Then north over little country roads through Van Cortlandt Park.

"We're clear of the patrols now," Vanhelb said.

They struck the Post Road, and Vanhelb spurred his horse to a fast trot. To Haym Salomon it seemed wonderful and almost impossible that they should be riding this way in the moonlight, without fear of pursuit. The drumming of their horses' hoofs sent a clear message through the night, but the British were far behind them.

They went on like this for some time, neither of them speaking, each rapt in his own thoughts. Then Salomon seemed to hear something behind him.

"I think we're being followed," he said.

"It wouldn't be the British this far north. Thieves, if anything."

Vanhelb spurred his horse to greater speed, and Salomon followed. They drummed along. Turning in his saddle, Salomon made out vague shapes in the rear.

"Their horses are better," Vanhelb said grimly. He

54

turned in his saddle and fired his musket. "Can't hit anything at night from a saddle," he explained. "But that
will let them know we're armed and ready for them.
They'll keep their distance, or I miss my guess."

He was right. The highwaymen hung on for half an
hour more, but then they dropped back out of hearing.
Vanhelb slowed his pace.

They rode on at an easy trot. A while later, Vanhelb
pointed to dark blurs on the road ahead.

"What is it?"

"We'll see in a moment," he said.

A barricade closed the road, and behind it were some
armed men. They wore no real uniforms, but there was
something about how they held themselves, a sense of dis-
cipline, that told Salomon they were no ordinary highwaymen.

"Who goes there?"

"Jan Vanhelb and an escaped prisoner from the British
jails."

"Advance slowly with your arms up."

A young man in uniform came around the barricade.
His uniform was old and patched and faded, yet it
marked him from the rest.

"Hello, Vanhelb," he said, and to Salomon, "My re-
spects, sir. Lieutenant Gregory of the Continental Army."

CHAPTER EIGHT

IT WAS hard for Haym Salomon to realize that he was among friends, that the strong arms of the Continental Army surrounded him. Even after a day had passed, even after Vanhelb had left with the escort of a few soldiers to take him through no man's land, he could not get used to the idea that danger no longer menaced.

He had been in the enemy's camp for too long. He would never get over the effect of the years in New York, when every move he might make for the cause he believed in would have to be undercover, when his work had been only to spy, to conspire, to help those who could not help him.

Here was American territory. It was a strange sensation for him to walk past the lines of weather-beaten, torn tents that sheltered troops of his country. Not since that day, so long ago, when Washington led his defeated army through New York to Harlem, had he seen a real force of American troops.

Certain things he had known; as, for instance, the terrible poverty of the American cause. He had heard how poor his infant country was, how there was never enough money to pay the soldiers, to feed them and to clothe them. But it was one thing to be told that and another to see it with his own eyes.

And now there was time enough to see it. As he wandered through the American encampments, the signs of poverty were all around him. In New York, he had become used to the well-fed, well-dressed British regiments. Each regiment had its own magnificent uniform; the British soldiers wore powdered white wigs. When they paraded in New York, the whole town turned out to see them, it was such a wonderful sight.

He wondered who would turn out to see these Americans if they paraded.

He would stand quietly and obscurely in the background and watch the Americans turn out for parade. Not one of the rank and file had a uniform. They were dressed in everything and anything, in old pantaloons and hand-me-down breeches. They made pathetic attempts to achieve a sort of uniformity. They thrust green twigs into their hats, those who had hats. They pinned strips of white linen across their chests. They bound rags around their legs to imitate leggings.

Their bayonets were bent and rusty, but they held their bayonets smartly as they paraded. They were not green troops, but seasoned veterans of years of revolution. They

57

might not look pretty, but they could fight. They had proven that at Saratoga and at Monmouth.

Some of the officers had uniforms that they had bought and paid for themselves, but even the officers' uniforms were old and faded and patched.

Haym Salomon saw how the soldiers ate. With all the plentiful harvests of the Hudson River valley, there was never enough food to feed them. The prosperous farmers preferred to sell their food to the British for good hard gold instead of to the Americans for the devalued Continental dollars.

And as for pay—well, Salomon listened to the men talk, and he talked with them. Most of them didn't have the same scorn for Jews that the British held. They liked the little man with the brown eyes who had escaped singlehanded from the Provost Jail. And they told him things. They told him how it was one thing to want to serve your country and another to have little to wear, less to eat, and no pay to send back to their families. How can a man go on fighting when he knows that his family back home may be starving?

Haym Salomon began to form a new picture of the revolution. The men in the armies were only a part of it. The Continental Congress was another part. And the farmers, the workers, the merchants, who supported the revolution, were a third part. And of the three, each was as necessary as the others. The army would have no purpose except for the Congress, which defined the aims of the revolution and gave the army a legal authority. And neither the army nor the Congress could exist without support from the farmers and workers and merchants.

Yet all three of them were spun together and held together by one single thread, and the more Haym Salomon saw, the more he became convinced of what that thread was—*money*.

Without money, the army could not stay in the field a single month. Without money, the Continental Congress would collapse like a punctured balloon. Without money, the revolution would fold up and fail.

There, walking among the poverty-stricken army of the republic, he realized what his work must be. Yet the thought of finding money and working with money only threw him deeper into despair. Even the clothes he wore were not his own. He was a penniless beggar, without a home, without a name, with nothing.

How could he even presume to serve his country by giving her some of the financial help she so desperately needed? He didn't know. He knew only that that was what he must do, somehow.

The troops which were encamped between Dobbs Ferry and White Plains were under the command of General Alexander MacDougall. MacDougall had been, years before, one of those Sons of Liberty, who had encouraged the earliest flames of the revolt in New York. At that time, Haym Salomon had known him, and since then word of Salomon's doings in New York had frequently come to the general.

Now, when he met Salomon, a flicker of recognition came into his eyes, and he smiled curiously.

"So we meet again, my little Jew," he said.

"Yes," Salomon nodded. "And you are a general, and they say you've done great things. And I'm an escaped prisoner, a penniless beggar."

MacDougall still smiled. "A lot might come of a Jew who can escape from the Provost Jail after the British sentence him to be hanged. I heard of that, and I also spoke to a Hessian deserter who showed up here in camp a few days ago. He said a Jew prisoner had talked him into deserting. I can surmise the rest."

"I'm glad the Hessian is safe," Salomon said.

"And what now? You can't return to New York until the war is over—if it ever is. You may have guessed how bad things are. It's poverty and hunger and nakedness we're fighting now as well as the British. Do you want to join our beggars' army? I hear you have a head for accounts, for the prices of things and buying and selling. I could use a man like you in the commissary department. Would you like a commission?"

"It's good of you to offer me that," Salomon said.

"But?"

"But I'm not a soldier. There's work for me, even if I don't know yet what that work is. But the work isn't here. You can't feed an army or a country by becoming a commissary officer."

"And how would you feed them, my little Jew?"

"I don't know. But the heart of the country, right now, is Philadelphia. If your men are to be fed and clothed, it won't be because one of your underofficers can drive a shrewd bargain with some Dutch farmer. Perhaps I have

60

an exaggerated sense of my own importance, but I feel I can do more than that."

"Perhaps you can." MacDougall nodded.

"Anyway, I can't remain here. I can't remain thirty miles from my wife and child, knowing I can't see them. Maybe I'm a fool. I'm beginning to understand, for the first time in my life, how big this revolution is. There's little that one man can do, unless he's a George Washington."

"I wish that more men could see that," MacDougall mused.

"Anyway, I would like to leave for Philadelphia in the morning. If you can give me a pass?"

"I'll give you the pass. And good luck to you. Perhaps we'll meet again someday."

"Perhaps we will," Haym Salomon smiled. "We all have a long path to travel."

CHAPTER NINE

TODAY, a journey from New York to Philadelphia means little. In fact, it can hardly be dignified by the name of "journey." Many people who live in New York commute daily to their work in Philadelphia, and many Philadelphians work in New York. Today, a person living at Dobbs Ferry, just above New York, can drive down to Philadelphia in two and a half hours, if it so pleases him, or he can go by comfortable air-conditioned train and make the trip in considerably less time.

In Haym Salomon's time, such a journey was a venture, difficult in times of peace, even more difficult in the midst of the Revolutionary War.

After many good-bys to the friends he had made, Salomon crossed the river at Dobbs Ferry and started southwest toward Morristown. He still had the pistol that Vanhelb had given him, and which the good man had insisted that he keep, and he still wore Vanhelb's homespun clothes, several sizes too large for him. But he had nothing else, and he couldn't accept any more than a few bits of dry bread and some smoked meat from the poverty-stricken soldiers.

Penniless as he was, he had made up his mind to walk to Philadelphia, a distance of something more than a hundred miles, or at least to the bank of the Delaware River, where he might sell his pistol and purchase seat space in one of the long, heavy keelboats that voyaged up and down the Delaware, from Philadelphia to twenty or thirty miles above Trenton. There was a stagecoach, running on a not too certain schedule, but riding a stagecoach cost money. And money was one thing Haym Salomon lacked completely.

He started out on a sun-drenched morning, scuffing his still good shoes in the dry dust of the highway. Those shoes had taken him a long way, and they would take him a long way more. They were good, stout cowhide, made by old Aaron Joseph, who still had his little booth on the Bowery. He would miss Salomon's trade now.

As Haym Salomon walked along, with the sun-flecked slopes of the Ramapos showing in the distance, with the good, clean Jersey air blowing against his cheeks, he tried to keep his thoughts from what he had left behind him. He thought then of how he and all his race bore the curse of the wanderers. There was no rest for them, no security; it was better for them if they did not remember too keenly what they had left behind.

63

Yet he thought to himself, "This country, it's so big, so splendid, so new. If ever there was a promised land where all peoples of the earth may live in peace, then this is it."

In spite of himself, he could not keep his thoughts from turning back to New York. He wondered whether his wife had heard that he was alive and well. As soon as he reached Philadelphia, he would manage, somehow, to communicate with her.

A farmer came along the road in the direction Salomon was traveling. He drove a crude two-wheeled cart, piled high with squash and turnips, and he bade Salomon good morning in the broadest Dutch.

He was so delighted when Salomon answered him in Dutch that he invited him to ride on the board seat beside him. The horse was old and fat and moved slowly, but for all that, it was better than walking.

"You're Dutch?" he asked Salomon.

"Polish, but I have a gift for tongues. Two weeks in a place and I'm talking glib as a parrot." Then he told the farmer how, years past, he had been in old Holland, in Amsterdam.

He rode with the farmer all morning, and the two of them exchanged memories of old Holland.

"It's good to hear of the old country," the farmer said. "The young folks are forgetting the language already. They want to speak nothing but English."

"Someday," Salomon said, "there will be nothing but English spoken in all the length and breadth of the land."

"Do you think so?" the farmer asked anxiously. "It seems a shame that the old talk should be forgotten."

Then they spoke of other things, of the prospects for the American forces. The old farmer hated change, and more than that he hated the American paper money. He told Salomon that he had in his attic a barrel of Continental dollars, which were not worth the paper they were printed on. Yet for all that, a son of his was fighting under General Washington.

"We Dutch don't forget how the British took New York away from us. We don't hate them, but America is not for them. It's for the people who come here from the old country to make homes for themselves."

Haym Salomon nodded. He was thinking of many things, of how the work of making a country would begin only when the war was over.

He left the farmer about midday, when the old man had to turn off the highroad to his farm. He wanted Salomon to come to his home and spend the rest of the day there, but Salomon would not let anything turn him from his path to Philadelphia. He thanked the old farmer, and the Dutchman, surmising that he had no money, suggested:

"A smart fellow like you, he could write out letters at sixpence apiece. Folks around here have a son or a brother in the army, or out across the sea, and there ain't many of them can write."

Salomon nodded, thanked the farmer, and put the idea away for future use. He had never thought of turning his hand to public letter writing, but the sooner he

65

had some silver lining his pockets, the better off he would be.

All the rest of the afternoon, Salomon walked on down the road. Twice he was challenged by little bands of ragged Continentals, but each time his pass from General MacDougall saw him safely through. While the country was at war, right now no campaigns were in progress. The British held New York City, and the Americans held Philadelphia and most of the countryside between there and New York. Each waited for the other to make some move.

As evening approached, Haym Salomon began to look about for some wayside inn. Before, he had planned to spend the night in some haystack or abandoned barn, but now he decided to follow the farmer's suggestion and put his skill as a letter writer to work.

He came to a heavily timbered building, with a sign out showing that it was called the "Blue Heron Rest." The Stars and Stripes hung over the doorway, but Salomon was quite certain that somewhere the innkeeper had folded away a Union Jack. Innkeepers were adepts at changing their allegiance to whomever were their best customers. In front of the inn, a post coach was changing horses and a number of men lounged on three-legged stools in the shade.

Salomon nodded at them and entered the inn. The main room was a combined kitchen, taproom, and dining room. At one end a great fire burned to take the chill out of the late August night and over the fire chickens, geese, and a suckling pig turned on a spit.

"At any rate," Salomon thought, "they eat well out here, even if our soldiers starve."

The landlord came up to Salomon, rubbing his hands and smiling. "Fine evening," he said, "fine evening. Dinner? A room? A glass of grog?" He was a little sallow man, with a heavy stomach that came of over-indulgence with his own food.

"All that I would like," Salomon nodded. "But I have no money."

"No money!" The smile on the landlord's face froze up.

"Yet I have some skill at writing letters," Salomon said. "I thought perhaps for a bed and a bite of food I could write whatever letters you may have need to send. In a nice hand, too, well rounded and easy to read."

"And what makes you think I can't write for myself?" the landlord demanded.

"I don't doubt but that you can," Salomon said. "Yet a man as busy as yourself—how often can he collect his thoughts and sit down to write letters?"

"You're right there," the landlord agreed. "It's a man's work, running an inn. Those fools ask me why I'm not in the army. I say, let me see you run an inn for one week and show a profit, my fine friends. Yes, there's little enough time for me to get letters written."

Soon the landlord had Salomon settled behind a table with pen and ink and a pile of foolscap paper. He wrote to his sister in Maryland and to his brother in Virginia. He wrote to two aunts and an uncle in various other states. He wrote a condescending letter to a nephew who was serving very valiantly under General Anthony

Wayne. Then, rummaging through his memory, he found a grandmother in Scotland, whom he had never before considered worth the price of sixpence to the public letter writer.

"A man should never forget his grandmother," the landlord said pompously.

A second cousin in Boston completed the list. Rack his mind as he would, he could find no one more to write to.

Now the other guests had come into the inn, and seeing how Haym Salomon was employed, several of them hired him for sixpence to write them letters. As a result of the evening, he had several shillings, a good, hot meal, and a bed.

Haym Salomon was up with the dawn and on the road. He might have bought a few miles' passage on the coach, but he considered it wiser to save the little money he had and go on walking.

Anyway, the weather was fine, the days not too hot and not too cold. The tall maples on the Jersey hills were ruddy with colors of fall, and the sky was clear blue, fleece lined.

And there was always someone on the road to pass the time of day with, militiamen going back to the army after the fall harvest, strolling peddlers, fur traders, coming in from the West to New York with their precious cargo, jugglers, beggars, families going West to find new homes.

Once, Haym Salomon dived into the brush at the side of the road while a patrol of British dragoons thundered

68

by. He wondered what they were doing so deep in American held land.

He managed another night's sleep in a wayside tavern, exchanged for his skill in writing letters and adding accounts. And there too he added a few more shillings to his purse. Sometimes, the thought made him laugh at himself—that he, the poorest of all men, should hope to support one day the financial affairs of his country.

As he walked along, he made many plans, yet his common sense told him that a beggar can do little planning.

The third night he slept in a farmer's barn, and the fourth night in a haystack. And on the evening of the fifth day, he reached the bank of the Delaware River.

He had to wait until the next morning before there was room on a boat leaving for Philadelphia. It took two of his precious shillings, and even at that price he would have to take his turn at the oars.

Yet it was a relief, after all the walking he had done, to sit back and watch the wooded shores of the river slide past. The old shoes were not so sturdy any more; there were holes in the bottoms and also in the uppers.

The boat's passengers were a motley crowd, men and women, old and young, but all looking forward to their arrival at the greatest city in the thirteen united states.

By evening, they were all more or less acquainted with each other. When darkness fell, they pulled the boat up onto the bank and built a roaring fire. They sat close to the fire, singing songs and trading food back and forth.

They were on the way again early the next morning.

Salomon had the first two-hour shift of pulling at the oars. A light, cold rain had started to fall. He was wet, tired, and uncomfortable. Then he heard someone call: "There she is!"

He twisted in his seat and saw the houses and docks of Philadelphia.

CHAPTER TEN

PERHAPS Haym Salomon felt that here, at Philadelphia, he had come to the end of his long, long journey. Perhaps he had some inkling that he, cursed with the mark of the wanderer that all Jews bore, would wander no more. A man's life is not laid out before him, yet many men, faced with the single important fact of their lives, have recognized it. Perhaps Haym Salomon recognized it too.

At first, after disembarking from the long keelboat, after saying good-by to the friends he had made on the journey, he stood on the dock for a time, staring at the scene that made up the waterfront of Philadelphia.

At that time, Philadelphia was the largest, the busiest, the most prosperous city in all the American states. Its population was almost thirty thousand; a good bit, if you remember that in all the thirteen states there were less than three million people. And these three million were predominantly a rural population. America was not an industrial nation in those days. It was a land of farmers, and by its farms it lived. So that a city of thirty thousand was a great city indeed.

During the winter of 1777-1778, while Washington and his men suffered through the awful cold and misery of Valley Forge, the British had occupied Philadelphia. There, for a winter, General Howe and his forces held court. They quartered their men on the Philadelphia people. They did their very best to turn the city into a smaller London. They held dances and balls and masques, great dinners and small dinners. They set the Philadelphia tailors to work turning out even more splendid uniforms than they had brought to America from London. They made friends of Philadelphia ladies, and many Philadelphia ladies, considering that the revolutionists were little more than a band of filthy, worthless beggars, made friends of the British.

And during all that winter, a little more than twenty miles from Philadelphia, George Washington held together the starving, freezing remnants of a defeated army. From December to June, this tall, seemingly cold, terribly enduring man who was one day to be the first president of an America not yet born, fought against worse enemies than the British: hunger and cold and the dread specter of dissolution.

At any time during that winter, General Howe, who had almost twenty thousand men at his disposal, might have attacked the three or four thousand at Valley Forge and destroyed them. If he had, the revolution would have ended then and there. There might have been no United States of America, and you might not be reading the story of a man named Haym Salomon.

But the winter was too cold, and General Howe was too comfortable in Philadelphia. He said to himself, "Only a fool would go after those Americans now. Cold and hunger will take care of them better than I could and with much less trouble on the part of everyone concerned. If any are left in the spring, there will be time enough to fight them then."

So, with such philosophy, General Howe threw away a great victory and thus helped to create the United States. For when spring came, not only were there Americans left at Valley Forge, but their numbers had started to increase. Farmers, through with their spring planting, picked up musket and powder horn, filled their pockets with bread and meat, and set off to join this man called Washington.

A certain Prussian came to Valley Forge, too, a Prussian whom Haym Salomon was later to know and befriend. His name was Baron von Steuben, and because he loved liberty and hated the military castes of Germany, he came to America and offered his services to Washington. And Washington, knowing good men, accepted those services.

So when the British at Philadelphia found time to pause in their wining and dining to survey the American situation, they found, much to their consternation, that instead of winter having destroyed the Americans at Valley

Forge, it had hammered them into a true force of revolutionary soldiers. Steuben had taught them the grim art of the bayonet; he had cleaned the rust from their cannons and showed them how to load with grape and fire with deadly effect. Thousands of recruits had swelled the ranks of the decimated Americans, and Steuben had turned these recruits into soldiers.

Telling themselves one thing and another, the British stayed on in Philadelphia until June, and then, in spite of the fact that they were still a good deal stronger than the Americans, they decided that they were not strong enough to attack them. In New York, there was another British army. Therefore, the British decided, the sensible thing to do would be to join their compatriots in New York, and then, with increased strength, turn on the Americans and destroy them.

Of course, they expected General Washington to concur in this decision and to stand calmly by while they carried out their purpose.

They marched out of Philadelphia as gaily as they had lived there, bands playing, flags flying. Many of the lovely ladies who had so adored the British went with them. Many whole families of Tories also left with the British.

And now Washington saw his chance. Trumpets sounded at Valley Forge, and the Americans swung out, circled ahead, and struck the long, sprawling column of the British a terrible blow on the flank, a blow from which the British were never to recover. This was the Battle of Monmouth, and the turning point in the war.

And the Americans had won back their great city. Never again were they to surrender Philadelphia. The ragged troops of Washington marched into the city half naked, but wholly victorious. They wore no uniforms other than wounds and rags and sprigs of green cocked in their hats. They were men of the revolution, farmers and workers.

It was only a matter of weeks after this reoccupation of Philadelphia by the Americans that Haym Salomon arrived there. Yet already it had become the capital city of America. Congress had returned from its exile to sit again in Independence Hall. Philadelphia was buzzing and humming and drumming with the lifeblood of the nation.

To Haym Salomon, standing at the waterfront of Philadelphia, there was a difference between this and New York as broad as the difference between day and night. The Delaware was crowded with vessels, brigs and schooners, great square-riggers and fast little sloops. And all over the wharves were piled barrels and boxes and bales, cotton and flour and tobacco and hemp and timber and iron, casks of gunpowder, unassembled fresh-cast cannon, bales of paper, baskets of fish, rolls of linen and silk and velvet, barrels of salted beef and pork, all the commerce and wealth of the states.

Nowhere was there the fear and hesitancy of a New York whose commerce had been strangled by the British.

So long did Haym Salomon stand there and stare at this evidence of healthy, active commerce, that he had almost forgotten his hunger. Now it brought him back to himself, and seeing a little stand kept by a woman, where bread and cakes were sold, he went over and bought himself a threepence loaf.

"Hard money," the woman demanded, meaning that she did not want any of the paper money issued by the Continental Congress.

"So even here," Salomon thought to himself, "with all the commerce and prosperity, a peddler will not take the government's printed money."

Breaking off pieces of his loaf and eating while he walked, Salomon wandered among the docks. To him, coming of a people who had always been the commercial explorers of the world, the scene was as fascinating as any he had ever observed. He saw husky stevedores unloading the boats that moved in a constant stream from the merchantmen to the docks. He saw commission merchants with their pads making an accounting of the goods. He saw brokers contracting for merchandise and bickering over price.

He saw the swaggering crews of privateers and blockade runners come ashore, rocking along arm in arm, singing their songs of the sea. He saw staid owners talking with their captains and planning new ventures.

Then, as now, blockade was a potent weapon of war. And the British had clamped a blockade on all the thirteen states of America. But to declare a blockade was one thing; to carry it out and make it actually airtight was another.

American skippers were the boldest that sailed the seas,

and American shipbuilders built the speediest ships. The rewards for running the blockade were very high. In the West Indies, American products were bringing fantastic prices, and in America products from the West Indies brought just as fantastic prices.

So if three ships started out to run the blockade and only one of the ships got through, blockade running was still profitable.

Again, there were the privateers. During the revolution, America had no regular navy. And they were fighting the greatest sea power in the world. Something had to be done, and Congress and the American sailors did it.

Congress issued letters of marque. These documents gave a ship's captain the legal right to prey upon enemy commerce. The American seamen did the rest. They fitted out their merchant vessels with cannon. They slipped through the blockade. And then they sailed out over the seven seas, destroying British commerce.

So bold were they that they sailed into the North Sea, into the English Channel itself. And when they returned to America, their holds were bulging with the loot they had captured.

All this Haym Salomon saw that first day he was in Philadelphia. And he saw more than that. He saw that a nation's life depends upon its commerce as much as upon its armies.

He saw, perhaps, the future of his land, when the commerce of the world would flow in and out of its ports.

CHAPTER ELEVEN

HAYM SALOMON left the waterfront and took his slow progress through the streets of Philadelphia. This was the kingdom he meant to conquer, and here, for however long it might be, was his battleground. He had come to a conviction, and that conviction might be stated thus:

"That the final campaigns of the revolution would be enacted more in the trading marts of Philadelphia than on battlefields."

England, since 1776, had made her greatest effort, and that effort had failed. From now on, America's strength would increase and England's—in America—would decrease. And America had gained a very powerful ally, France.

Yet that American effort must be flagged unceasingly.

78

And the lifeblood, the financial foundation of that effort, would flow from Philadelphia.

A good campaigner must know the terrain of a battlefield before he goes into battle. And from this day on Philadelphia was to be Haym Salomon's battlefield. The small, brown-eyed, now penniless Jew did not yet know how he was going to serve his country, but he knew that he would serve her in the way he knew best, in the field of finance.

For three hours he wandered through Philadelphia, and there was little that his keen eyes missed. He stopped before Independence Hall, where the Congress of the United States was sitting once more. He stood in front of the house where Robert Morris, the Superintendent of Finance, lived.

In spite of his worn and none too prosperous appearance, he went into two coffeehouses he knew of, and with his remaining silver had a pot of coffee in each. In the Philadelphia of 1778, these coffeehouses were the centers of trade. There the brokers and the merchants and the bankers gathered, to deal with one another, to buy and to sell, to exchange news about prices, markets, goods. In the coffeehouses, one could always hear the latest news of the war. In the coffeehouses, one could get the best opinion on the financial situation in France, in England, in Holland or Spain.

If you wanted to know the price of a barrel of flour in Havana, or a bushel of onions in Charleston, a coffeehouse was the place to go. If you wanted to know exactly how many decent pairs of shoes the Continental Army possessed, that news might be found in a coffeehouse.

Haym Salomon kept his eyes open and his ears alert. Right now, all he desired was to sense the drift of commodities. What was being bought and what was being sold. What fetched a better price in the West Indies than in Spain. A beggar cannot put such information to any real purpose, but Haym Salomon felt that he would not be penniless for long.

He heard, for instance, that you could buy a barrel of flour in Philadelphia for six dollars. Attle was selling for six, and Henderson, a smaller dealer, was selling for five dollars and seventy-five cents. Some of the independent millers outside the city might sell you a barrel for five dollars, or even for four-fifty.

Now that same flour would bring anything from twenty-five to thirty-five dollars in Cuba. That was a profit of six hundred per cent, if you could run the merchandise through the British blockade. And in Cuba, a pound of sugar could be purchased at a fifth of the price it would bring in Philadelphia.

It made his head reel to see what profits a man could make out of the war. Yet when he had come out of the coffeehouse, into the cooler air, he said to himself:

"But is that what I want? How many of those men in there are thinking of anything else but to become wealthy?"

Certainly, as a pauper, he could do nothing. Before he could do anything worth the effort, he must have money, money with which to buy and sell and establish himself in the world of finance. Yet there was one thing he must remember always and never forget: that wealth was not an end in itself, but rather a means to an end.

With him, the end must be one thing and only one thing, a free and triumphant America.

Night was falling, and Haym Salomon still walked the streets of Philadelphia. He came to a large house, in which a hall on the ground floor was lighted. Something made him stop to look through the windows. He saw inside a group of men gathered for worship. They had their backs toward him, and they were bent in prayer. The scene, a silhouette of dark swaying figures, impinged gently and warmly upon Salomon's consciousness. As he stood there, his throat swelled and his eyes became moist. Through the windows their low voices came to him.

At that time, in Philadelphia, the Jews had not yet built themselves a synagogue. Instead, they worshiped in a rented hall. Perhaps it was the sight of them this night, in that rented hall, which later made Haym Salomon one of the moving spirits in the construction of the first synagogue in Philadelphia.

As Haym Salomon stood there, a wave of bitter remorse must have overcome him. If in the past weeks he had thanked God in his heart for preserving him, he had done nothing else. In the excitement of escaping from New York, he had let his devotions slip far, far into the background. He was a religious man, and he had been brought up in a religious home. Yet for weeks now, he had neglected his religion.

With his head bowed, he went into the synagogue. A few of the men there turned curious eyes on the stranger, but not for long. Whosoever entered the synagogue was welcome.

He went to the shelf where prayer books and prayer shawls are kept for those who are not regular members of the synagogue. He took his place at the end of one of the last pews and opened the prayer book.

The first lines his eyes rested upon were these: "How goodly are thy tents, O Jacob, thy dwelling places, O Israel."

His eyes clouded with tears. Yes, here was his home, and this humble hall was the dwelling place of Israel. Here in Philadelphia they stood at their prayer, and no man's hand was turned against them.

He joined in the service. His voice blended with the others, and he felt a deep sense of security and peace.

When the service was almost over, the rabbi said, "If there is anyone here who has a request—"

Haym Salomon came forward slowly, and all eyes were turned to him. "For myself nothing," he said. "God has preserved me only too well. But when I escaped from the British prison in New York, I left behind me my wife and child—"

"May God preserve them," the rabbi said.

And the congregation echoed, "Amen."

Afterward, Haym Salomon had to tell his story five times over. He found the Jews of the congregation remarkably well informed on the entire revolutionary situa-

82

tion, and the questions they asked him were keen and very much to the point.

He found that many of them had stayed in Philadelphia during the British occupation and had done the same sort of undercover work that he had pursued in New York. Others had left Philadelphia and came back to find their homes ruined and ransacked.

Many were the offers of help and encouragement he received, and most of the men were very cheerful on the subject of his wife and child. The British would not dare to imprison a woman. Word could be gotten to her through wandering Jewish peddlers; gold the same way. The British had not yet learned that Jewish peddlers had eyes and ears, and very often what the eyes saw and what the ears heard went straight to American army headquarters.

Many insisted that Haym Salomon come home to dinner with them. He was so grateful that he could not keep his eyes from blurring with tears. An hour ago he had been a homeless, penniless wanderer; now he had friends enough.

He finally accepted the invitation of a grain merchant, Jacob ben Casro.

It was strange for Salomon to feel the warm spirit of family life again. Casro insisted that he accept a change of clothes. They were old clothes anyway, Casro apologized. But after wearing the old, ill-fitting, dirt-stained homespun for so long, Salomon felt like a king in the fine broadcloth coat and the doeskin breeches.

Salomon bathed and shaved himself and then combed

83

the burrs and sand out of his hair. He tied his hair carefully in a pigtail, as was the fashion of the day, and then went downstairs to dinner.

Casro introduced Salomon to his wife and two children. Mrs. Casro was a stout, matronly woman, who couldn't believe that such a frail creature as Salomon had endured what he had. The two children stared in wide-eyed wonder at this man who had escaped from a British prison.

During the dinner, more or less by common consent, they avoided talk of the war, of Salomon's journey, and of New York under the British. Salomon praised Mrs. Casro's cooking, and she filled his ears with current gossip of Philadelphia. And, indeed, it was almost more than Salomon could believe, to find himself seated here with this warm-hearted family, eating good food, well cooked, at a table set with shining silver, gleaming china, and white linen.

The meal progressed toward its satisfying finish, and then Mrs. Casro and the children left Salomon and the merchant alone at table. The grain merchant filled two glasses with brandy and offered Salomon a fine black cigar, taking one for himself.

"You've been too good to me," Salomon protested.

"Not at all. Actually, what you've suffered and lost has been for a cause that's mine as much as yours. And I think all of the Jewish community in Philadelphia feels that way."

"I'm glad to hear that," Salomon nodded.

"But glory is one thing and the practical business of

84

living is another. Have you thought about what you will do? It will take money to get your family out of New York and bring them here."

"I know that," Salomon nodded.

"And your plans, if I may ask? I heard you were quite successful in New York, in spite of the British having their eye on you interminably—morning, noon, and night."

"I have plans—or no plans, depending on how you look at it," Salomon mused. "If I didn't have a wife and child, I might join the army—"

"No, that's not for you. For one thing, Washington has enough men now. Last year, it was men he needed. This year, something more."

"I know that too. And that something more, I also realize. An army is no good unless you can feed the men, pay them, and clothe them. And right now our country is terribly near to bankruptcy, so near that it seems to me we are tottering at the edge of a precipice. One step farther and all Washington's work is undone." Salomon hesitated. "That is part of the task I had set for myself— I know it's too much for one man, for a dozen men. Yet if I could have only the smallest part in it, well, I'd feel that I had repaid America something for the hope it gave to me and to my people."

"Have you any money?" Casro asked.

"Nothing—not even twopence. All that I lost in New York. Well—it amounted to perhaps thirty thousand dollars. That's gone now, and there's no use thinking about it."

"You have nothing," Casro smiled. "Isn't it a rather large task you're setting yourself?"

"Maybe it's too large," Salomon murmured. "I don't know. I can only try."

"Some people would be satisfied enough to earn a living, just to pay the rent on a house and feed and clothe their family."

"I was in Poland," Salomon said. "I was born there, I lived there. And in almost every other country in Europe I also lived. Do you know what it is to be a Jew in Europe? Do you know what it is to be herded into ghettos, to be forbidden to worship, to till the ground, to read books, to listen to music, to send your children to school—to be forbidden all that? Do you know what it is to be spat upon, to be considered more a beast than a human being?"

"I know," Casro nodded. "My people were driven out of Spain. They went to Italy. They were driven out of Italy, and they went to Portugal. They were driven out of Portugal, and they went to Brazil. How long does it go on? Forever. They were driven out of Brazil, and they came here at last, to Philadelphia. How long before Philadelphia drives them out?"

"Never!" Salomon cried.

"I think you believe that," Casro murmured.

"Yes, I believe it."

Casro stared at the smoke of his cigar. "Salomon," he said at last, "I want to do something for you—not so much because you're a Jew but because I like you. I like the idea of a little man, beaten around the world, yet

86

still trying to save that world—even if it is a Gentile world."

"America will be a world for all men," Salomon said, as if he were repeating a creed he could never doubt.

"Will it? Sometimes I almost believe that myself. Now understand, Salomon, I'm not doing this out of generosity, but because I believe you could help me. I'll give you a job as clerk in my grain house, at a good salary too."

Haym Salomon shook his head slowly. "You're very good to me," he said. "I appreciate what you're doing. You're very good to a stranger. But that isn't what I want. I have to be free. Even if you laugh at the work I've set for myself, I have to be free to make my attempt. I can't work for any man. I can't be bound to any man."

"I'm not laughing at you," Casro said, a trace of anger in his voice. "But what can you do without money?"

"Nothing."

"And will you make money out of thin air?"

"Perhaps. If I have to, I'll make it out of thin air. I've done it before, and I'll do it again."

Casro shook his head, as if he had never met with such a person before. "At least a loan?"

"I have to be free," Haym Salomon said. "I'll take loans when I feel I have some prospect of repaying them. Now I have no prospect at all."

"You admit that?"

"For the time being I admit it."

"Well, then let me give you this bit of sound advice," Casro told him. "You lost a fortune of thirty thousand dollars in the service of your country. At least, petition

87

Congress to take some notice of that fact. What the Jews are doing in this war will be soon enough forgotten. It's not the sort of work men remember. You owe it to yourself and to us to petition Congress."

"I'll do that," Salomon nodded.

"And there's nothing else?"

Salomon smiled. "One other thing. You're a man of sound business reputation in Philadelphia. On the other hand, I am unknown here. If Haym Salomon says something in Philadelphia, people have no reason to take him at his word. If someone comes to you tomorrow or the next day and says, 'What about Haym Salomon? Is his word good?' will you vouch for me?"

Casro hesitated. "You're asking a great deal."

"I'm pledging my word to you. It won't be broken."

"I'll vouch for you," the merchant agreed.

CHAPTER TWELVE

Finest

Tobacco

T HE following day, Haym Salomon wrote the letter in which he petitioned the Continental Congress. He began his letter this way:

"To the Honorable, the Continental Congress:

"The Memorial of Haym Salomon, late of the City of New York, merchant, Humbly shewith,

"That your Memoralist was sometime before the entry of the British Troops at the said City of New York and soon after taken up as a Spy and by General Robertson committed to the Provost. . . ."

He is referring here to his first imprisonment, in 1776, after George Washington and the American forces had evacuated New York and left it in the hands of the British.

Then he went on to tell how he had been released by

89

Lieutenant General Heister, "who wanted him on account of his knowledge of French, Polish, Russian, and other Languages."

Another passage in the letter told of his service to escaped American and French prisoners, and then, farther on, of his escape from New York.

He also mentioned the sum of the property he had lost in New York, and the fact that he had been forced to leave his wife and child behind him when he escaped.

He ended the letter very curiously. As yet, he had no business in Philadelphia, yet he petitioned Congress to grant him some favors in the business with which he was engaged. Perhaps already he was seeing the pattern that would shape the next few years of his life.

Of course, the whole petition was more of a formality than anything else. As Casro had said, it was a good way of putting on the record what would otherwise soon be forgotten. And that Salomon owed more to others than to himself.

At that time, in Philadelphia, the Continental Congress was in such a state of confusion, that they could hardly have paid any more attention to Salomon's petition than to the dozens of other petitions that were pouring in.

You must remember that they were sitting in a city which had just been vacated by the enemy. Whatever orderliness the revolution has in history books, it had no such orderliness in actuality. It was not a series of well-planned, well-executed campaigns. It was a wild, uncoordinated struggle of thirteen states for liberty. And these thirteen states were as different from one another, as far

90

from one another in traveling time, as Bulgaria is from France today.

If you think of the Spanish civil war in our own time, it will give you a better idea of the American revolution than any history book.

And Congress sat in Independence Hall, trying to bring sense and order into this far-flung struggle. Petitions poured in faster than they could be read. Demands poured in. This general needed five hundred pairs of shoes or else his army must sit down and stop fighting. That general needed shirts. This captain was leading a company of men who had no breeches. Was that a thing for the British to see, men without breeches calling themselves American soldiers?

This general had not paid his men in five months. A brigade refuses to be paid in American paper money because its value drops each day. A thousand dollars needed, five thousand dollars, ten thousand dollars . . .

Try to picture this Continental Congress as it was, the first Congress that had ever sat down to govern America as a nation. What would happen today if a Congress sat in Washington that had had no experience in government or politics?

One word might describe it—it was a mess, a complete mess. The delegates struggled and only got deeper and deeper into the mess. The cry for money was a clarion call, heard from one end of the land to the other. Everyone needed money, for this and for that, and of money the Continental Congress had very little.

As for American paper dollars, which, at least, Con-

gress could print to its heart's content, they were prac-
tically worthless. The reason is this: A paper dollar is
merely the promise by a government to pay in gold or
silver the amount printed upon the paper. If you will look
at a dollar bill, you will see on it, "One dollar, in silver
payable to the bearer on demand." That means you can
take your dollar bills into any bank and cash them for
silver dollars. The reason no one does this is because it is
very inconvenient to carry a pocketful of silver dollars.
The paper is easier to handle.

But what would happen if everyone in America, at
once, doubted the ability of the government to redeem its
dollar bills? Simply this: There would be a rush for silver
and gold—"hard money"—and merchants would refuse
to accept the paper money in payment of debts. Farmers
would not sell their food for paper money, but only for
silver and gold.

Perhaps, in the beginning, merchants would say, "Give
me one silver dollar for this article or two paper dollars."
In other words, the price of things in paper money value
would go up. And because prices in paper were going
up, the government would have to print more and more
paper.

This happened in Germany after the first World War.
Paper money became worthless. For a dime you could
buy a million marks.

And in America, at the time of the revolution, the same
thing had happened. The Continental Congress printed
money and said, "Sometime, when the war is over, we
will redeem this money."

But people were afraid to accept the American paper money. Suppose England won the war? The money would be worthless. So, as a result of that, the money lost its buying value. The saying was that it took a barrel of paper money to buy a barrel of flour.

Still, Philadelphia was a thriving, prosperous city. Commerce flowed through it. When the British left, not one merchant ship floated on the Delaware, and now more than three hundred ships lay at anchor. You may ask how this commerce was carried on if American money was worthless. The answer is that buying and selling was done in the coin of a dozen nations, English shillings and pounds, Dutch thalers, French francs, Spanish pistoles, the minted coin of the various states, such as the "pine-tree shilling" of Massachusetts, old pieces of eight; in fact, every sort of coin and money under the sun except American paper money. Prices were reckoned in dollars, but dollars were not used for buying.

And amid all this plenty, the revolution steered its shaky course through the shoals of bankruptcy. Congress, ever bedeviled by pleas for money, could find money nowhere. It was little wonder that they could find no time to give to Haym Salomon's petition.

But Haym Salomon did not waste time worrying over the effects of his petition, once it was drawn up and sent on its way. He had work to do, and there was precious little time in which to do it.

The following morning he made his way down to the docks and spent a careful hour wandering among the piles of merchandise, listening to the commission agents and noting the price of various products. It was still early in the morning, and he tried to sense what might be in rising demand. He kept his ears open and heard that two ships carrying tobacco from Cuba were long overdue.

Tobacco was selling at eight dollars a keg. Salomon calculated quickly, decided that he would have to plunge sooner or later, and then took a deep breath. He approached an agent who was checking a mound of tobacco kegs.

"How much do you have there?" Salomon asked.

The agent glanced at Salomon, did not recognize him as one he knew, and kept at his work.

"Why?" the agent demanded over his shoulder.

"I'm in the market to buy," Salomon said carefully.

"Two hundred and fourteen kegs," the agent said brusquely.

"At what price?"

"Do you want one keg or five kegs? I'm selling at eight dollars."

"I'd take all of them at a fair price," Salomon said.

The agent whistled and turned deliberately to face Salomon. "What do you call a fair price?"

"Seven seventy-five a keg."

"Seven eighty and sold," the agent said.

"Done," nodded Salomon. "You'll make delivery, I suppose?"

"Any city warehouse. I'll need cash."

"I'll pay on delivery," Salomon said calmly.

"Well, I don't know you, sir. Never done business with you before. What's your name?"

"Haym Salomon."

"Never heard of you, I'm sorry to say. Mine's Allen. Now look here, I'm willing to hold this tobacco for you, but I got to have a deposit. Suppose a couple of tobacco ships come in and the market falls. I could start selling now at eight dollars a keg."

"You'll have to hold on my word," Salomon said calmly.

"I don't know your word, mister."

"You know Casro, the grain dealer?"

"I do. An honest man, too."

"He'll vouch for me," Salomon said. "Will you give me a bill of sale?"

"Conditional until tomorrow at noon."

"Very well," Salomon said.

All that day, Salomon watched the tobacco prices. Until about four in the afternoon, they held steady; then a slow rise began. That evening, when Salomon showed up at Casro's house, the merchant smiled and said:

"I see you didn't waste any time. Allen came around to see me, and, as I promised, I vouched for you."

"I hope I won't be a pensioner on your bounty much longer," Salomon said.

"That's all very well. But are you sure you know what you're doing, Salomon? You've contracted to pay for two hundred and fourteen kegs of tobacco by tomorrow noon —at seven dollars and eighty cents each. That's a lot of money, and I'm bound to support your contract. Suppose a tobacco cargo is unloaded first thing in the morning and the price drops to seven fifty?"

"That's a risk I would prefer to have taken myself," Salomon said. "But since you took it for me, I give you my word that I will repay whatever loss you incur."

"Seems you've given your word to half the people in Philadelphia," Casro said testily.

"Not yet," Salomon smiled. "But I hope the day will come when half the people in Philadelphia know what my word is worth."

Early the next morning Salomon showed up at one of the coffeehouses. As he did not even have enough silver to buy a pot of coffee, he sat quietly on one of the benches and listened to the trade talk.

Finally, prices on tobacco were quoted. The two expected ships had not yet come in, and tobacco was up to eight and a half dollars a keg. Buying began, and the price rose to eight fifty-five.

At this point, Salomon said in a low but clear voice, "Gentlemen, I have two hundred and fourteen kegs that I will sell at eight dollars and thirty cents, cash on delivery before noon."

They turned to him, stared, and then rushed to buy at a price below the market. In ten minutes, Haym Salomon had disposed of his tobacco.

A day's work, a good guess, and a gamble had turned him from a penniless wanderer into a businessman with a clear profit of one hundred and seven dollars.

CHAPTER THIRTEEN

HIS work was under way now, and once Haym Salomon had plunged into that work, he never paused. His first deal must have been considered by many a lucky guess. Casro shrugged his shoulders and said, "Next time he won't be so fortunate." However, if it was luck, Haym Salomon continued to be lucky.

Thanking Casro for his hospitality, Salomon took a room for himself. From dawn until dusk, he explored the financial structure of Philadelphia. He was not content with what he heard; he had to see. And the only way to see was to get into every odd corner of the city. He ranged through the streets of Philadelphia until he knew them as well as he had ever known the streets of New York.

He spent long hours on the docks, talking to the cap-

tains of the blockade runners and the privateers. Many
were the wonderful and fascinating stories that he heard.
He spoke to hard-bitten seamen who had traded in the
ports of the French coast, under the nose of the British
fleet. He listened to the tales of thin-lipped privateer
captains who had come into port with the spoil of a dozen
British ships.

A few captains, some of the crews, and many super-
cargoes on the privateers were Jewish. They were the
same sort of hard, seafaring Jews who had sailed with
Columbus on his first trip to America. They spoke a
curious English, heavily interspersed with Spanish, and
their faces were Spanish too: long, hawk nosed, and
brown.

At first they were amused by the small, brown-eyed,
gentle-speaking Jew who wanted to know all there was
to know about the sea and its ways. They held aloof, since
he was a Polish Jew, and they, as Spanish Jews, considered themselves his superiors. But it was not difficult
for him to win them over. He had a certain assurance
about everything he said. And he was very diffident, giving more credit to their exploits than they had ever
granted themselves. They came to like him, and they
showed their liking by imparting expert information,
which captains were careful and which captains were
reckless, where the British blockade patrol was likely to
be this week or next week. Often they suggested that
he come along on one of their cruises, warning him about
his hard, hacking cough.

"That cough will be the death of you yet," they said.

98

"That cough— Well, it's a gift of the British. Twice they had me in their jail under the gentle Cunningham, and each time I came away with something more. Yet I'm lucky. Others never came away."

"A sea voyage would cure it."

"I have so little time," Salomon would explain.

He made many friends on the docks, but he did not neglect the other parts of the city, the coffeehouses especially. The coffeehouses played the part of stock exchanges, clearing houses, trade marts, and bargain houses. In the coffeehouses loans were made, goods sold, money raised, and, sometimes, the very fate of the nation decided.

The rich men of America sat in these coffeehouses, and again and again Salomon was shocked to see how little they cared about whether the revolution succeeded or failed. For most of them, the revolution was merely a means of increasing their wealth, and this they callously, even brutally, went on with. If one of them had, in a warehouse, ten thousand pounds of flour, and the British were paying more for flour than the Americans were, then he would be sure to see that the flour went to the British. They bought and sold and speculated with only one end in sight—profit.

That men had suffered and died for the revolution meant nothing to them. That men like Washington were striving like gods for a free America also meant nothing to them.

Of course, some had consciences, but they were in the minority. Most of them looked upon the revolution either as a period of speculation during which their one duty was to make money or else as a period of uncertainty, which interfered with and ruined business.

Haym Salomon had known before what business meant and what international businessmen were, but never had it been so clearly brought home to him as now in the coffeehouses of Philadelphia. Again and again he doubted himself and his purpose.

"Where am I going?" he would ask himself. "Wouldn't it be better for me to enlist in the army? I could do little enough good that way, but I could at least die like a man in the company of men—men who believe in something. This way I am pursuing something vague as a ghost. I need money to do what I intend to do. I have to follow the path the monarchs of the coffeehouses take. And they have no other god than gold and no other purpose than to fill their pockets."

For all that, he persisted. And to be a Jew in the coffeehouse marts of exchange was not pleasant. He had to bear insults and scorn and hatred. The epithet for everything vile was "Jew."

If two men were driving a bargain, one would be sure to say: "Stop jewing me down!" Or when talk ran high and mean, someone would say, "You're acting like a synagogue full of Jews!"

They referred to Salomon, not by his name, but as "That Polish Jew—" as if the name of Poland had not been made wonderful by all the Poles who fought and died in the ranks of the Continental Army.

100

Or else, "That damned Jew, that haggling Jew—"
His profit was referred to as "his pound of flesh."

For all that, he persisted. He alone among them had
the power to see beyond the coffeehouses to the America
that might be someday. He alone never wavered in his
faith in the eventual triumph of George Washington.
And since he based most of his speculation upon the
eventual triumph of American arms, he prospered
quickly.

It was not long before he was able to rent a little office
in Front Street and announce in the papers that he was
ready to deal in bills of exchange and whatever other
securities people might feel they were willing to entrust
to him.

And that was not a presumption. The few people he
had already had business dealings with were saying,
"Haym Salomon—a man you can trust. Good as his
word."

One of the first visitors in his office on Front Street was
a bearded Jewish peddler, a pious wanderer who carried
his prayer books in one hand and his pilgrim's staff in
the other.

He made a strange figure as he entered Salomon's
office, first touching his hand to the *mezuzah,* Biblical
passages in a case fastened to the doorpost, and then to
his lips. He set down his pack on the floor, a pack bulging
with ribbons, trinkets, bits of silk, bracelets, rings, neck-
laces, brooches, all the odds and ends of women's finery

101

that were so rare in frontier America and so welcomed by women on isolated farms, who had little enough opportunity to make themselves lovely.

"*Shalom alekhem,*" he nodded to Salomon, words which are Hebrew for "peace unto you."

"*Alekhem shalom,*" Salomon answered. "Unto thee, peace."

The peddler was a tall, spare man. His heavy, dust-covered shoes showed that many miles had flowed under his feet. He wore leather breeches and a homespun coat, and his broad-brimmed black hat was tilted back on his head. He had small blue eyes that twinkled merrily, and as was the custom with pious Jews, he kept his hat on all the while he spoke to Salomon.

"And what may I do for you?" Salomon asked, after he had invited his visitor to have a chair.

"Something, Haym Salomon, and perhaps I may do something for you. My name is Isaac ben Levi, and as you see, I'm a peddler. Not the best life for one whose destiny was to be a Talmudic scholar, and whose days should have been spent in devoted study. But not the worst life either. I have a pack of this and that, and as you may have guessed, sometimes I turn an honest penny. My feet are hard, and I walk here and I walk there. People become accustomed to seeing me. Even the British no longer question me. And if I see this or that worth remembering in a British encampment and write it down and stuff it deep into the bottom of my pack, who will bother to empty out the junk that a Jewish peddler has to sell?

102

"And if later that same bit of information comes into the hands of an American officer, who will remember the old Jewish peddler?"

Salomon stared. His heart trembled with hope, but he scarcely trusted himself to speak.

"Yes," the peddler went on, "when I was in New York I rested my weary feet in the house of a good woman. Her name was Rachel, a good, old name in Israel. I told her how my feet take me God only knows where, and she gave me a letter. Later on, having some information for the American General MacDougall, I showed him the letter. He said, 'Your man is in Philadelphia, I believe.' So here I am in Philadelphia."

"Where is the letter?" Salomon whispered.

The peddler smiled and gave it to him, and Haym Salomon read the first words he had had from his wife in weeks. She was alive and well, and so was the baby. She lived only in hope of seeing her husband and being with him again, if God permitted. Salomon read the words again and again, before he turned to the peddler and asked:

"How was she?"

"Well enough. But worrying about you. I told her that God will provide for all of us."

"And the baby?"

"As healthy a baby as I ever laid eyes on."

"I don't know how to thank you," Salomon said. "I don't know how to thank you enough."

"Don't thank me. If you have any thought of repaying

103

me, bed and board for the night will be payment enough. And now if you are going to the synagogue, I'll go with you. I have been too long in the wilderness."

All other thoughts were crowded out of Haym Salomon's mind that night. They were at Casro's house, and he and the peddler and several other members of the Jewish community discussed ways and means of bringing the family out of New York and into Philadelphia.

Moses Gomez, a sea captain, suggested sailing into the harbor some night in a little sloop and putting her aboard right under the noses of the British. But the others dismissed that as too risky.

One plan after another was suggested, and finally the decision was to put the whole matter in the hands of Isaac the peddler. He would return to New York, obtain a boat somehow, and then, on a dark night, ferry the Salomon family across the Hudson onto the Jersey shore. Then before dawn they could enter the American lines and get coach passage to Philadelphia.

The days passed slowly after Isaac had left Philadelphia. Haym Salomon tried to plunge into his work, tried not to think of what was going on in the muted, British-guarded streets of New York. During this time he met Aaron Levy, one of the most active of the Philadelphia Jews in support of the Revolution. Levy had already come to realize the fine sense of finance Salomon had, but when Salomon spoke of aiding the American cause, Levy shook his head.

"It's more than any man can hope to do. This Congress

104

is so deep in the waters of bankruptcy that the whole
thing seems hopeless. What can you do? Or any man—"

"I'm trying to believe that will be shown to me when
the time comes."

"I only hope it will not be too late then," Levy said.

Haym Salomon went on with his trading, his buying
and selling. So far, outwardly, he was not very different
from the rest of the coffeehouse traders. A little more
honest, less demanding upon his debtors, less inclined to
drive a hard bargain, less inclined to reach for huge
profits.

Yet he needed profits and he made profits. Men no
longer sneered when they spoke of the Jew broker of
Front Street. They realized that a man had entered their
circle who was bigger, in their own field, than any of
them. A man who knew finance, who knew Europe and
America.

Salomon found that he needed someone to assist him
in his work. There was a certain Scotsman, a man named
McCrae, who had done ledger work for many of the
coffeehouse group.

One day Salomon approached him and said, "You
know who I am, I suppose?"

"I've heard of a little man called Haym Salomon,"
McCrae smiled. He did not smile very often. He was a
lean, dour Scotsman, who considered a smile as something to be hoarded, not wasted on every occasion.

"You might have said, 'The Jew Salomon.'"

McCrae shook his head. "I don't hold with them who
curse the Jews for every trouble on earth. I've seen good

105

Jews and others not so good, like with any other folk."

"It's funny," Salomon mused, "that you hear so often of a Jew and a Scotsman being in business together."

"Maybe because they've both of them got a head on their shoulders, eyes to see with, and a nose to smell out the way things are drifting. But what are you getting at, Mr. Salomon?"

"Just this. My business is increasing, and I need someone to do the office end of it, keep the books, follow prices and interest rates. I need a man I can trust and who would trust me. Would you like to work for me?"

The Scotsman eyed Salomon a moment, then said, "You know, I make a fair to middling living here."

"I'll pay you fifteen dollars a week to start," Salomon said. "More after, but that now."

Fifteen dollars then was the equivalent of sixty or seventy dollars now. It was a good salary, a fine salary.

"Done," McCrae said.

They shook hands over what was the beginning of a partnership that would be dissolved only by death.

It was about two weeks after the first time Isaac the peddler had appeared that he again knocked at the door of Salomon's office. But this time, when he entered, there was behind him a woman with a baby in her arms.

At first Salomon stood there, unable to speak, just staring at his wife. The peddler smiled at the two, then slipped away without saying a word.

But Salomon and his wife never noticed. They just stood there, too overcome to speak.

106

Then Salomon came forward and looked at the baby. He touched its cheeks cautiously. The baby laughed.

And Haym Salomon saw that his wife was crying. "Don't cry, Rachel," he said. "Everything is all right now. Everything is fine now. Don't cry."

"I thought—"

"Don't cry."

Then she and the baby were in his arms. And all he could think of was to tell her over and over again, "Don't cry, Rachel, don't cry."

"When they took you away—"

"I know, Rachel. But that's all over now."

It was some time before they could sit and look at each other and smile. Haym Salomon sat with his baby in his arms, playing with the child. And his wife never took her eyes from him, as if she could never see enough of him.

He had to relate over and over all that had happened to him since he was taken to the Provost Jail that night. He had to tell of his escape and his journey through the British lines. But he made light of everything.

"That's the past," he said. "Here, in Philadelphia, I'm building a new life for us."

"They took everything we had," Rachel said. "Even the house, in the end. They thought you would come back, and they watched the place day and night. I prayed to God you wouldn't come back. They would have shot you down like a dog. Then they quartered soldiers in the house."

"But they didn't harm you?"

"No, they didn't harm me or the baby. But everything is gone, everything. How will we live?"

"Then you don't know?"

"Nothing. Old Isaac told me you were well, but nothing else. Where did he go? How can we thank him enough?"

"He'll be back. And as for living, we'll live well enough. I'm doing well here in Philadelphia, buying, selling, trading in securities. Here in Philadelphia, a man can make a fortune."

"I don't want a fortune. As long as God has preserved you—"

Haym Salomon said earnestly, "I want to believe there's a reason for that, Rachel. I'm trying to do something here. I don't know how to begin, where to begin, but I think I can do it. This country is being wrecked even before it comes into existence—by financial failure. I want to try to stop that, somehow."

CHAPTER FOURTEEN

THERE came a period now during which Haym Salomon devoted himself to only one purpose, that of building up his reputation as a broker and businessman of unquestioned honesty and dependability. He worked furiously, so furiously that again and again Rachel pleaded with him to rest, to stop for a while.

And always his answer was the same. "But there is so little time—so very little time."

She would ask him what he meant by that, but he never fully explained it to her. He wasn't quite certain himself that it was only aid for the revolution, which was needed desperately soon. Sometimes, when his racking cough took hold of his whole body, when the spasms went through his chest like fire, when his eyesight blurred

109

and his senses reeled away into darkness, he had an awful fear of his own impending doom. But when the spell had passed, he would feel full of reckless, consuming energy.

"I'm a young man," he would tell himself. "People in my family live to a ripe old age, and so will I."

But once, during a coughing spell, he felt a hot pain in his throat. He wiped his mouth, and when he took the handkerchief away, it was red.

He kept that from Rachel, but to reassure himself he went to see a doctor. In those days, doctors knew less of medicine than the average high-school student knows today. Yet this doctor had seen other persons with this unmistakable symptom, and he knew what the inevitable consequences were.

"You have to rest," he told Salomon. "Rest and more rest and still more rest."

"And otherwise?" Salomon asked.

"Otherwise?" said the doctor. "My dear young man, if you do not rest, perhaps there will be no otherwise."

"I see," Salomon nodded, smiling curiously. "Yet I don't think I can rest. There is too much to do, far too much to do. How can anyone rest these days?"

The doctor shrugged his shoulders. He didn't have too high an opinion of Jews. Ever since someone had told him that the medicine of the Jews in fifteenth-century Spain was superior to that which he practiced, he had clung to a stubborn dislike of Jews.

"If I don't rest," Salomon said slowly, "then how long will I have?"

110

"How long? I don't know. Maybe a year, or two years, or if you're lucky, five years. Six shillings, that will be."

Haym Salomon paid the six shillings. He was very thoughtful as he walked from there to his office, but when McCrae saw him enter, Salomon was smiling eagerly.

"Good news?" McCrae asked. They had made a speculative contract for a portion of the goods on an overdue privateer. It was a custom, in those times, when a privateer was overdue, for the owners to hedge on their risk; in other words, to sell a percentage of their cargo to anyone who would still take a chance on the privateer coming into port safely. In this, the profit was great, but the risk was also greater than that involved in most business deals. It was, actually, a primitive form of ship insurance.

"Good news? No, the *Gull* hasn't come in yet."

"You looked pleased," McCrae said.

"And I am. Do you like a good fight?"

"That, I do," McCrae nodded sagely.

"Well, we're going to fight time. We're going to fight it as it was never fought before."

And leaving McCrae to mull over that, Salomon went to his work.

Meanwhile, Rachel was happily engaged in the business of setting her household in order. Haym Salomon had taken the rest of the house on Front Street, where his office was located, and had turned it into a home for himself and Rachel.

111

As for Rachel, she was more than delighted. She could not believe that in the whirl of events, God had been so good to her. She had to stare again and again at the little brass plate on the front door, which said, simply, HAYM SALOMON, BROKER. She had to polish it over and over until it gleamed like the very sunshine.

For her, it meant more than its simple statement that a broker was doing business inside the house. For that broker was her husband, and of what wasn't he capable? Hadn't he slipped out of the British jail like a ghost? Hadn't he gone through their lines the same way? Hadn't he walked to Philadelphia, coming there penniless, and wasn't he a respected businessman now? Whatever he said, that he would do. She never doubted him. What a life they would have together!

She lavished all her care upon the house. It was not of red brick with an angled Dutch roof like their house in New York, but half timbered with mellow, ancient smoky wood. Instead of the Dutch ovens she was used to, there was a great fireplace in each room. Part of it was furnished in rich old maple. For the dining room, she found a plain, American-made set of oak, which, plain though it was, delighted her with its sturdy strength. She wandered through the narrow, cobbled streets of old Philadelphia until she found a Chippendale couch, which, the cabinetmaker assured her, was by the hand of the master himself.

Haym Salomon, who had eyes and ears only for his work, realized suddenly the change that her hands had wrought in the house.

112

A HAPPY FAMILY

"My little wife, you're very wonderful," he told her.

"No—only very happy."

"Is there anything more I can give you?"

"Nothing, nothing at all."

He continued to hide his cough from her, his occasional hemorrhage. The doctor had said a year, or five years. Perhaps, if God were good to him, it would be ten years.

McCrae began to understand what Salomon meant when he spoke of fighting time. He caught him once, bent over, racked with the pain of his cough, and he saw the blood that stained Salomon's lips. In the months they had been working together now, he had come to hold his little employer in the greatest esteem.

"Can I help you?" he asked Salomon.

"No, not with this. Only, don't tell Mrs. Salomon. She must never know."

"But, sometime—"

"No, we're living only for the present. There's work to do now. The future will take care of itself."

The privateer *Gull* came into port with the rich booty she had taken from nine British merchantmen. Once more, Haym Salomon had played his hunch and had guessed right. His percentage amounted to seven thousand dollars.

Now, in the coffeehouse, they no longer sneered at "that Jew Salomon." Instead, they came to look at him with a certain amount of awe.

"Those Jews," certain of his less lucky colleagues would say, "everything that they touch turns to gold."

115

Almost correct, but not quite. That night, at the Salomon home, a little celebration was held. Haym Salomon, his wife Rachel, and McCrae sat at table together. They had opened a bottle of wine, and they were merrily toasting one another and the captain of the *Gull*.

There was a knock at the door. It was Aaron Levy, strangely serious and anxious.

"Salomon," he said, "I would like to see you."

Salomon nodded and invited him to sit down.

"Alone," Levy said.

They went into Salomon's office. The two men faced each other, and Levy studied Salomon intently.

"You have been doing well," Levy said finally. "Amazingly well. They say everything you've laid your hand to has gone in your favor. Already you're spoken of as a rich man."

Salomon nodded. "That's true."

"It does things to some men when gold begins to flow into their hands."

"Are you afraid that it will do something to me?" Salomon asked.

"I don't know. You're a strange man, Salomon. There seems to be a demon in you, burning you up, driving you on. To what purpose?"

"I saw one country die," Salomon said slowly. "I saw Poland torn to pieces. I saw a free country lose its freedom. It wasn't because Poles were afraid to die for what they believed. In America they showed only too well that they were willing to die for freedom. America must win,

116

do you understand? Not only for our people, but for all men. There is hope in America, if nowhere else in the world. There is a part for me in that struggle for America."

"And how do you propose to play it?" Levy inquired. "By amassing riches?"

"That's the first step," Salomon nodded.

"I hope you're right," Levy said anxiously. "I hope nothing will change you."

"When a man walks with death," Salomon smiled enigmatically, "his purpose is not easily changed."

"I don't know what you mean by that," Levy replied, shaking his head. "But this, actually, is what I've come here to see you about. These are bad times; few people know how really bad they are. Everyone thought that after Burgoyne's surrender, after Monmouth, the war was as good as won. They considered that the alliance with France would put us beyond defeat.

"Well, perhaps it has, in a military sense. Yet in another sense, we are nearer defeat than ever before. But this is a defeat that will come from within ourselves. An enemy worse than any massed forces of armed men is on our heels. I mean bankruptcy.

"I think you know something of that, but let me explain a little more before you say anything. We'll take one detail, the pay of men in the army. The coffeehouse crowd may rant of liberty, which to them means filling their pockets, but even a patriot can't fight for freedom unless he has some income to feed the family he left behind him. Now when the war started, pay was fixed. A colonel, for instance, earned ninety dollars a month, a captain forty-five dollars a month, a private seven dollars a month. Not a great deal, you will admit, but perhaps ample to keep their families alive if not happy.

"But what has happened? I guess you know only too well what our paper money is worth. And these men are being paid in paper money—do you understand? There is nothing else to pay them with except the paper money. Now if we grant paper money its quoted exchange value —and it isn't actually worth that—what do we find? A colonel is being paid three dollars a month, a captain a dollar and a half a month, and a private—the men, mind you, who are fighting this war—a private is paid twenty cents a month. Do you understand that? Twenty cents a month. But when he takes his paper money, which is nominally worth twenty cents, and sends it to his family who try to spend it, it is flung back into their faces. Because it's worth nothing really, not even the paltry twenty cents.

"And to make this madness merrier, the English have begun to counterfeit our poor paper money. Not for their profit, but for our distress. They're flooding the country with thousands and thousands of dollars in Continental bills. They couldn't defeat us on the field of battle, so they're taking the easier and surer way. They're driving us into bankruptcy. They know there's no money to feed the men, to clothe them or pay them. They know that when finally our credit breaks, the bottom will drop out of the revolution. The men who haven't starved or frozen

118

to death will go home. The revolution will be over without another shot being fired."

Salomon nodded, and then for a little while the two men sat in silence. At last Levy broke the silence by clearing his throat and saying:

"Do you still believe, Haym Salomon?"

"I have four thousand dollars here in my office," Salomon said. "You know, I had taken overdue percentage shares on the *Gull,* which came into port today. It still hasn't docked, and then the goods will have to be auctioned. But my share is reckoned to be about seven thousand dollars. Meanwhile, there is the four thousand dollars—in English pounds."

"You realize, of course, that this money may never be paid back?" Levy asked him. "I have gone to the others of the synagogue, and what we give will be given very quietly. There will be no shouting and no drums and little chance of repayment."

"I know that," Salomon nodded.

"Four thousand dollars is a great deal of money."

"I wish there was more."

Levy smiled strangely. "I won't thank you, Haym Salomon. This sort of thing is forgotten too quickly. It's better if you have no thanks. You will go on believing, even if the echo of a gun resounds longer than the clink of a silver dollar."

When Haym Salomon came back to the celebration in the dining room, he was curiously happy. He felt that his work had really begun. The future was not yet entirely clear, but it was taking shape.

They were doing some business now in bills of exchange. There were many sorts of bills of exchange in Philadelphia that year and the next.

Modern banking is international; it is a machine that operates with remarkable ease. Here is an example: if America makes a loan to Great Britain today, it involves no transatlantic movement of cash. Say the loan is ten thousand dollars. The American bank making the loan will simply write ten thousand dollars off its books and at the same time open an account for ten thousand dollars in the name of Britain. If Britain wishes to spend the money here, the bank simply honors its checks. Now suppose the money is to be spent in England. In that case the American bank again writes ten thousand dollars off its books, but instead of opening the account in America, it opens it in a British branch of its own bank, or else in a British bank. No movement of cash is necessary.

But in the time of the revolution, this was not the case. A foreign loan would be made in the form of a bill of exchange. Business with foreign countries was also done that way.

The bill of exchange was more or less of a check or an I O U or promissory note. For example, if France were to make a loan to America in those times, they would send across the Atlantic a bill of exchange, say, for ten thousand dollars. Now, although this was considered a loan, it was not actually a loan in cash. It was a promise by France to pay to the bearer the face value of the note.

The bill of exchange itself was of no value to the government. It had to be sold first, converted into cash. And

120

the person who sold it had to endorse it; in other words, to make himself responsible for payment of the note in case France refused to pay. This is particularly important, since so much of the revolutionary financing was done upon this basis.

But the bill of exchange also figured in business. A man in France or in the French West Indies, buying American merchandise, would often make payment with a bill of exchange instead of cash. It was safer to do so than to transport cash across the seas in those uncertain times. Again, that bill had to be sold or converted into cash in America before it had any real value.

You might question why anyone should buy these bills of exchange. Well, if a man needed money and had a bill of exchange with a face value of one hundred dollars, he might sell it for ninety dollars in order to raise cash quickly.

In that way, Haym Salomon, having a keen knowledge of the currency of other nations and of the prices of exchange, began to do more and more business in these bills.

He had his own place in the coffeehouse now. Men would come to Haym Salomon with this and that and anything. He was a man who could be trusted. His investments in privateers and blockade runners increased, and most of his investments paid well.

Yet for all that, he was not satisfied. The work he had set for himself was still undone. What little money he could give to his government would not save it.

121

It was some months later that Levy said to him, "How does it go with the young revolutionist?"

"Well enough—only—"

"Only you are coming to realize that you cannot save America alone. You're right—no one man can, not even Washington."

Salomon shook his head. "I won't believe that it's over —I can't. It's all I live for now."

"What do you want to do?"

"I don't know," Salomon said miserably.

"It was better when you were escaping from the British, wasn't it?" Levy prodded him. "It was better when your only interest was Haym Salomon and preserving Haym Salomon's life. It would have been better, even, if you had become a soldier. You could have died quickly and easily that way. You can't stand to see the revolution destroyed when you see so clearly what is destroying it."

"You're right. I can't stand that," Salomon admitted.

"And what do you intend to do?"

"I don't know—I don't know what there is to do. If I give, if we all give, it still won't save us."

"It won't. The treasury deficit is nearing a million and a half dollars. And Congress has not yet awakened. Congress won't tax the states. Congress won't take hold of things. You and I buy a hundred barrels of flour, a hundred uniforms—but what difference does that make? You can't maintain three armies in the field with a hundred barrels of flour."

"Still, if Washington—"

"Wait a moment," Levy said. "There's a man Washington believes in, a financier like yourself. A little mad, but fiery, very much like yourself. Try to see him."

"What is his name?"

"Robert Morris," Levy said.

The third and final chapter in the life of Haym Salomon was about to begin.

CHAPTER FIFTEEN

WHO was this man, Robert Morris? Levy had suggested that Haym Salomon seek him out, yet even before Levy had spoken the name, Salomon had suspected that he would say, "Robert Morris."

He had heard much of Robert Morris, and again and again he had wondered when his path and that of Morris would cross. He had seen Morris at the coffeehouse, although Morris did not appear there very frequently.

Now he began to wonder. He had wanted to do his work alone. Yet the more he pried into the financial background of the revolution, the more he realized that no one man could perform the task he had set for himself. Even Robert Morris was not succeeding in holding back the crest of bankruptcy, and if Robert Morris, in whom

124

men believed, in whom Washington himself had placed his confidence, could not succeed, then how could Haym Salomon?

He asked himself this question again and again. He said to himself, "This business of finance, this whole underground struggle to keep the nation out of bankruptcy, is just as much war as any battle that has been fought. Then if I am serving in that end of the war, under whom am I serving? Alone, I seem to accomplish nothing."

He said to McCrae, "What do you know of Robert Morris?"

"A smart man."

"Is he honest?" Haym Salomon demanded.

"Some say he is and some say he isn't."

"But what do you think?" Salomon insisted. More than once he had cause to admire the Scotsman's keen estimate of men.

"I think he is. I think that without him this war would have been a far blacker mess than it is. But they won't let him work his own way. They keep bedeviling him—the Congress, I mean. And what he's trying to do, no one man can do."

There it was again, Haym Salomon's own thoughts. "Do you think," Salomon asked, "if someone he trusted worked with him—if he found someone he could depend upon?"

"Who?"

"Haym Salomon, perhaps—"

The Scotsman eyed Salomon narrowly. He said, "Mr. Salomon, when our books showed a thousand dollars less here, a thousand less there, I asked nothing. I said to myself, 'The money's his to do what he pleases with.' But I think that because of that money, men marched and men ate and men were clothed. And when they were clothed, they were clothed with a uniform instead of rags—the uniform of the American army. You can trust me," he finished.

"I can trust you," Salomon nodded. "But what I did was very little, almost nothing. If I had any purpose in conjuring money out of thin air, it was to make that money serve my country. Now I find that I have failed. I can earn a thousand or ten thousand dollars, but not the hundreds of thousands that are needed."

"You've done enough," McCrae said.

"Enough? Do you call nothing enough?"

McCrae shook his head.

"If only I could get Morris to trust me, to believe in me," Salomon mused. "I could help him. I'm not boasting, McCrae, when I say there's no man in Philadelphia who knows what I know about exchange, about international currency."

"You're not boasting," McCrae agreed. "But Morris—I don't think he leans to Jews."

"Then I must make him know me," Salomon said quietly. "Then I must force myself upon his attention. Even if I must crawl toward him, I must make him realize that there's a man called Haym Salomon who can serve his country."

"It's little thanks and less happiness you'll have out of it."

126

"The thanks I can do without. The happiness will be for those who come after us, Mr. McCrae, not for us."

And who was this Robert Morris?

It is strange that the two men who more than any others carried on the dark and underground struggle for America, the struggle against bankruptcy and ruin, should have been so wronged by those who wrote history.

As for Haym Salomon, his name was forgotten.

As for Robert Morris, generations of men blackened his name more and more. A small lie, once started, gathers weight with its own momentum as it rolls along. And there was more than one lie flung against Robert Morris. It was said that he robbed his country to enrich himself. It was said that he cared only for wealth. According to two men who attacked him very bitterly, Arthur and William Lee, the revolution was a godsend to Robert Morris. They say that the revolution came along just in time to save him from personal bankruptcy, and that the revolution brought him wealth, contracts, and large profits.

How much truth there was in such accusations we shall see presently. It is enough to say that if any two individuals forced the American revolution along its bitter course to final victory, then those two were George Washington and Robert Morris. Lies were flung at both of them, but both emerged from the welter of lies, still clean in their own unselfishness.

Actually, Robert Morris fought the revolution as steadfastly as any man of his time. Far from enriching himself at the expense of his country, he almost ruined himself. For all the work he did, none of the glory was his, just as none of the glory was Haym Salomon's.

The lies mounted against him, just as lies will gather against any man whose ability is a little greater than the ability of the men around him. But through all, Morris never swerved from his purpose, which was to serve America and the revolution.

Robert Morris was born in Liverpool, England. And here is a point for a curious commentary. You must understand that, to understand why that war was called a revolution. It was not a war fought against a foreign nation, but a revolution within the body and structure of English-speaking peoples. Englishmen fought on both sides, and when America emerged victorious, it was not only America that had triumphed, but also underprivileged, English-speaking people all over the world and in Great Britain itself.

At the age of thirteen, Morris came to America, alone. You can imagine that his struggles were as difficult as the struggles of any immigrant boy would be today. He learned that for a boy of thirteen, alone and friendless, the world was a hard place. It was a lesson he never forgot, even when he himself had become wealthy.

Later his father followed him to America. His father, who had started as a workingman, and had then accumulated a comfortable fortune as a merchant, died soon after his arrival in America. He left seven thousand dollars to young Robert. And in those days, seven thousand dollars was the equivalent of fifty thousand today.

Robert was then a clerk in the Philadelphia commercial house of Willing. At the age of twenty-one, Morris joined the firm, having increased his inheritance considerably. The firm became Willing and Morris, and such was Robert Morris's commercial sense that he soon headed the firm. He went on to make it the leading firm in Philadelphia and then the leading firm in America.

Robert Morris was for the cause of independence, but his commercial training made him wary of rushing headlong into anything. For that reason, on July 2, 1776, he voted against the resolution for independence. He thought that the movement was premature, that the colonies were in no way prepared for war with England, and he did not doubt, as others did, that war would follow. When the Declaration of Independence was drawn up, he refused to vote for it. It was adopted; then he did sign. However, his reluctance was considered by many as a symptom of Tory leanings.

This was not so, but Robert Morris was the sort of man who was hard and violent in his opinions. He made friends slowly and enemies quickly. His knowledge of finance and commerce was so much more complete than the accumulated knowledge of Congress, that to him they seemed like a pack of fools, waving their arms and crying aloud to thin air, "Money." He knew how necessary money was to the successful carrying out of the war, and he knew that money could not be obtained simply by stamping paper in a press, as Congress proceeded to do.

George Washington, who early in the war learned what might be expected, turned to Robert Morris after

Congress had disappointed him in all his pleas. Washington was driven to desperation by his need for money. He knew that the war would not be a short one: He knew that long years of campaigning lay before him. He also knew that his chief duty during those years would be to preserve the army intact.

Yet to keep an army of from ten to fifteen thousand men in the field without money to pay them or clothe and feed them was a task beyond the ability of any man. Time and again, Washington pleaded with Congress for money. Time and again he told them that without money the whole movement for independence would go to pieces.

Yet to all his pleas, they answered one excuse or another. For this, Congress was not entirely to blame. They had no real authority to tax the separate states. They were not actually a central government. They did their best, but their best was not a great deal.

So in his desperation, Washington turned to Robert Morris. The story goes that once, being in immediate and desperate need, Washington applied to Morris for a huge sum of money.

The harried financier took stock of his resources, sought about him for ways and means of raising money, and drew a blank at each place. Finally, in a very despondent mood, Morris walked through the streets of Philadelphia, as if he expected the very paving stones to give up an answer.

Walking along, he met a Quaker, a friend of his. He had not gone to the Quakers for money, though they were one of the wealthiest groups in the city. Their principles were against war in any form for any reason, and though many of them sympathized with the revolution, few gave it active support.

"What ails thee, Robert?" the Quaker inquired.

Morris spilled out his story. He told how low the ebb of American success had sunk, although that was not a new story. He told how all his sources for raising money had failed.

"Robert, what security canst thou give?" the Quaker asked calmly.

"Security?" Morris thought of the security of a nation that could not raise a few thousand dollars in the hour of its need. "No security other than my note and my honor."

"Thou shalt have it," the Quaker said.

The next morning, Morris wrote to Washington, "I was up early this morning to dispatch a supply of $50,000 to your excellency. . . ."

A heavy, hard-headed, abrupt, plain man, with the taint of Liverpool slum speech still on his lips, this then was the person Haym Salomon had made it his purpose to seek out.

CHAPTER SIXTEEN

IT WAS one thing for Haym Salomon to believe that Robert Morris needed him. It was another thing for Robert Morris to come to hold that same belief. Twice Haym Salomon tried to see the financier, and twice he was rebuffed. Another man might have given up, gone on with his work, made himself wealthy on the profits of war.

But Haym Salomon refused to see defeat, either for himself or for his country. Months passed, months during which he consolidated his position in the trade marts of Philadelphia. By now, everyone in the coffeehouse was aware that a new and dynamic figure had arisen among them. Those who looked upon the war merely as a means for filling their own pockets began to fear this man who hated profiteering, who based all his speculation upon the

132

single principle that America would emerge victorious.

His house was rapidly becoming a center for the most radical element in financial Philadelphia. Fierce and fanatical patriots sat down to dinner with him, and with strangely rapt brown eyes he listened to their stories of the course the war was taking in each of the thirteen states. He had the sort of mind which could consolidate each of these bits of information, file them away, and then reassemble them when needed in a complete picture of America at war.

He found confirmation of a fact he had noted before, that hatred of the Jews increases in inverse ratio to love of liberty. The less men loved liberty, the more they were for reaction and the defeat of America, the more they vented their hatred on the Jews.

He had never been insulted by a revolutionist, but time and again he had been insulted by the Tories of the coffeehouse. The revolutionists had learned too well the meaning of comradeship.

His cough was growing worse, slowly, but nevertheless surely growing worse. One night he had a hemorrhage, and his low moans of pain awoke his wife.

"Haym—what is it?" she whispered in alarm.

"Nothing, nothing," he reassured her.

"You're sick."

"No, it's nothing."

But this time she knew. She helped him out of bed, helped him sit in a chair, coughing and strangling with pain. "Why didn't you tell me?" she said. "Why didn't you tell me?"

"Why should I trouble you with a little cough?"

But she held his hands, kissing them, and would not let go of them. For hours she knelt by him, holding his hands and trying to warm them.

He seemed to have a well of mysterious energy from which to draw. He was sick in bed for four days, and then the fifth day found him down on the docks, bidding farewell to the captain of a privateer he had helped to fit out.

"A long voyage," he told the hard-bitten Yankee skipper. "A hearty voyage and a safe return."

"Don't you worry, Mr. Salomon. I'll make her bulge with gold before the English see the last of me."

And then back to the coffeehouse. Flour was being bought by Congress to feed the army. He fought like a wolf to knock the price down. He bought and sold, each time shaving off the price. A slim, quiet figure, he lurked in the background. No one knew who was spreading rumors, engineering the market, yet steadily the price of flour fell and fell.

The word went around, "Salomon says the bottom's out of the flour market."

"Salomon says four wheat ships from France came through the blockade."

"Salomon says don't hold flour."

"Salomon says the Virginia crop was the best of the year."

And the government agent licked his lips and bargained harder than ever. He didn't know who his silent ally was; he didn't care. He knew that his mission was to buy flour as cheaply as possible.

And when Haym Salomon had finished, he had saved the government of the United States almost four thousand dollars.

He was off then for the tobacco market. On the street he met a Quaker, an acquaintance of his. After they had greeted each other and had spoken of the weather, Haym Salomon said:

"You know Robert Morris?"

"Somewhat."

"Tell him that if he will see me sometime I believe I can serve him."

After the tobacco market, he rushed home. A child was expected in the Salomon household. When he got home this day, the doctor was already there.

"Have patience—only patience," the doctor said.

He couldn't wait, couldn't stand still, couldn't pace the floor. He went into his office and harried McCrae.

"Where do you get your energy?" McCrae wondered.

"Any news from the front?" Salomon demanded impatiently.

"Quiet, too quiet. Something's brewing, something terrible and big—perhaps the biggest thing in this war."

"I knew it, I knew it," Salomon said impatiently. "They have to do something. They can't go on as they've been going on."

"They've done something," McCrae smiled.

135

"What?"

"Congress has appointed Robert Morris Superintendent of Finance."

"What?"

"With full power to raise the money needed to carry
on the war—"

"Thank God," Salomon whispered.

The doctor was pounding on the door. "A girl," he
told Haym Salomon.

The little man was staring away into space, smiling
strangely.

Now he waited. Now he knew that the time for him to
serve was near, and he waited—with strange patience for
him—to see how it would come.

He studied the exchange, watched the prices on bills.
He realized something of the trouble Robert Morris
would encounter in his efforts to convert bills of exchange into funds with which to run the government and
the war. The price on bills of exchange was dropping
lower and lower.

Many of these bills came from the French army in
America. They were drawn on banks in France and sold
by French officers so that they might raise cash to feed
their men. But so little skilled were these officers in dis-
posing of the bills that the price dropped lower and
lower. No person of repute would endorse the bills. The
market was flooded with them, and dishonest brokers
were demanding commissions of ten and twenty and
thirty per cent.

This drove down the price of American loans, which were sent from France in the form of bills of exchange. No one trusted these loans, and no one desired to convert them into cash.

Haym Salomon lost no opportunity to say to friends of Morris, "If he is ever in need, tell him to call on Haym Salomon."

And at long last the time came.

Another summer was over. The colors of fall were in the trees and in the sky, and the cold nip of fall was in the air. The high holy days of the Jews were approaching, and once again they gathered in their synagogue for prayer.

It was Yom Kippur, the holiest day of the year for a Jew, the Day of Atonement, when Jews fast for twenty-four hours and remain all day in the synagogue at their prayers.

The little hall was full to overflowing. Not only were the Jews of Philadelphia there, but also the men who had come from the armies in the field, men in torn, faded regimentals. They stood with the others, the striped prayer shawls over their shoulders, asking the forgiveness and mercy of God.

In the midst of the prayers, there was a knocking at the door. The sexton answered, and then a hushed whisper ran through the congregation. Haym Salomon was wanted.

He went to the door. A messenger stood there.

"This is our holiest of days," Salomon said impatiently. "Couldn't this have waited? From whom are you?"

"From Robert Morris."

"Give me that," Salomon said. He snatched the package, tore it open, and found two bills of exchange and a note.

The note was brief. It said:

My dear Mr. Salomon:

Here are two notes which must be discounted immediately. I have tried to raise the money, but found it impossible to procure within the time I have at my disposal. The need is great, the cause urgent. I have turned to you only because our distress could be satisfied in no other manner.

Sincerely,

ROBERT MORRIS.

"And today, on Yom Kippur," Salomon thought. "He turns to a Jew on our holiest day, when even the thought of money is forbidden. And he turns to a Jew only when everything else has failed."

A moment he hesitated, then tightened his lips. He looked at the bills of exchange and saw that each was for ten thousand dollars. Where could he raise twenty thousand dollars? Most of his money was tied up in privateers, in blockade runners. At the most, he had at his disposal a few thousand dollars in cash.

"Wait here," he told the messenger.

He walked through the congregation, which had returned to its prayer, and up to the pulpit. He touched the rabbi on the shoulder and said:

138

"I must talk to the people."

"But Salomon, have you lost your mind? This is Yom Kippur."

"And this is the cause," Salomon said grimly. "I must talk to them."

There was no withstanding the fire in his eyes. The rabbi gave place to him, and Salomon said, simply and quietly:

"The Superintendent of Finance has called on us. He has sent us two bills, which represent twenty thousand dollars. This money he must have immediately. I need not tell you what depends on it. If you will look around and see those of your number who are wearing the uniform of our country, you will know."

Murmurs came. "But Yom Kippur—"

"But the *cause*," Salomon said harshly.

It is as much of a sin for a Jew to write on that day as to speak of money, yet check after check was written. Salomon took them, one after another, his face hard and strange.

His own check was for three thousand dollars, all the cash he could raise at the moment. Not ten minutes had passed before the twenty thousand dollars was subscribed. The Jews turned back to their prayer.

He went to the messenger and gave him the money, and the man counted it quickly.

"But you've made no provision for interest," he protested.

"Tell Mr. Morris there will be no interest," Haym Salomon said.

139

THE incident of the synagogue had passed, but it left Haym Salomon a strangely changed person. Outwardly, he was not so different. He was still the small, inquiring Jew who seemed to be in all places at all times. He was still the curiously obscure ruler of the coffeehouse. His shyness remained with him.

Yet his friends noticed the difference, and sometimes those who were not so completely his friends. It marked itself in a tightening of his full lips; his face had become more drawn; and his mild eyes could now blaze in furious anger.

His struggle against time took on a quality of fanaticism. For the first time in his life, he began to hate—and anything opposed to the revolution came into the vortex of that hate. The businessman, the broker, had found his

140

purpose. He had not found it pleasantly. In his desire to serve, he had to beat his head against a stone wall of discrimination, scorn and abuse. But once he had battered down that wall, he allowed nothing to stand in his path.

Rachel loved him too much to let his singleness of purpose matter once he had come into the circle of the family. Then all things were to be forgotten; the war, the exchange, the complex financial swirl of Philadelphia. He was her husband and she was his wife. She took a deep and unceasing delight in the home she had established for herself in Philadelphia. Children came, yet there were never enough for her. She was the sort of woman who desired nothing more than to see herself surrounded by children, to watch them growing from childhood to young manhood and womanhood, to watch them play and laugh and live.

Yet for all that, she couldn't remain ignorant of the change. She saw the hardness creeping into her gentle husband. She saw the way he was driving himself, hard and without mercy. She saw his flesh thinning out, heard the cough rasping harder and harder.

She would ask him sometimes, "Haym, what is the use of all this, if in the end it destroys you?"

He would smile at her then.

"But don't laugh at me," she would plead. "Can't you see that you're not well, that you must rest?"

"Rest?" he would ask absently. "There'll be time later for rest. When this is over—"

"When this is over," she would say to herself, and then

she would remember the faces of the men who had been at Valley Forge that winter of 1777-1778, the drawn lines, the hard set of their mouths, the bitterness in their eyes.

"He is living for only one thing now," she realized. "Not for me, not for the children—but only for the revolution."

Morris's thanks were brief, and then a long time passed when he did not again call on Haym Salomon. But in that time, Haym Salomon was not idle. He saw one path that must be cleared before there would be any degree of economic security for America, and he set about clearing that path. He considered every possibility before he discussed the matter with McCrae.

As time passed, he and the Scotsman had grown closer. McCrae's devotion to Haym Salomon was almost as great as Haym Salomon's devotion to his cause. The two worked well together; one balanced the other. McCrae had a cautious, conservative mind; Haym Salomon, in anything concerning his beloved cause, was inclined to be reckless, utterly headstrong.

Now Haym Salomon put his latest plan to McCrae. He asked McCrae, "What would you say is the greatest obstacle to American financial stability?"

"Aside from a muddle-headed Congress," McCrae growled, "I would say right now the trouble is wildcat bills of exchange."

"Exactly," Salomon nodded. "My own opinion, but let me hear what you've got to say on the matter."

142

"In the first place," McCrae began, "every broker is cutting every other broker's throat. The bills of exchange are drawn on French banks, but what they'd be worth if we lose the war no one knows. Your guess is as good as mine."

"And as a result of that," Salomon nodded, "the brokers are underselling one another. They buy and sell and keep the market flooded with French bills of exchange. France is our ally now, and so long as she remains our ally and so long as General Washington can outmaneuver two British armies, the bills of exchange remain a good gamble."

"A good gamble but not a good risk," McCrae corrected.

"Have it your way. The point is this—that right now the ability of our government to function and continue the war depends almost entirely upon French loans, in the form of bills of exchange. Robert Morris has to sell these bills on the market and convert them into sound money before they are of any use to him. And right now he can't sell them. The market is ruined. The French loans are either no good at all, or if some of them can be sold for cash, a huge part of that cash goes to cover the risk the buyer is taking."

"And meanwhile," McCrae put in, "Robert Morris's hands are tied. And since his hands are tied, Washington can't act. If ever there was a time for one venture that would put an end to this war, now is that time. You're right about the market for bills of exchange. Until that market is settled and co-ordinated, there will

143

be no hope of any financial future for America. None at all."

"Yet if one person could stop this mad speculation on the bills," Salomon mused. "If one person could do that, then it might change the whole future of the war—"

"How?" the Scotsman demanded skeptically.

"Well, I have a plan. Most of the bills, outside of direct loans to America, originate through the quartermaster and paymaster general of the French army. Just as with us, the French army can buy nothing in America unless it first turns its exchange into cash. And the officers in charge of this have little experience and less regard for the paper entrusted to them. France is a rich country, and so long as they can draw on the mother country, they won't worry about keeping up the value of their bills.

"My plan is this, to gather all French army bills of exchange together and to sell them through one man. That man will endorse them, set the price, and never undersell that price. As a result, bills of exchange will stop fluctuating. They will have a standard value, just as money has."

"Except for one thing," the cautious Scotsman protested. "The man who handles them, considering that the French will agree to such a scheme, will have to endorse them. Otherwise, the situation will remain unchanged. And if he endorses them, and if the revolution collapses, he will be ruined."

"He takes that chance."

"And who will you find to take that chance?" McCrae demanded.

"I will."

144

"You're mad."

"I'm not mad," Salomon said grimly. "McCrae, I don't have to tell you that I'm a sick man. I don't speak of that, if I can help it; I don't think of it. But I'm a sick man fighting this war in the only way he knows of fighting it. And I'll go on fighting it that way. If I have to beat the French commander over the head to make him agree to my plan, then I will."

"I think you will," McCrae smiled. "Only remember one thing. Chevalier de la Luzerne is an aristocrat. I have learned that a Jew is not so different from a Christian. I have learned that more often than not the one is as much of a Christian as the other. Perhaps Chevalier de la Luzerne has not learned that yet. I don't want you to be hurt if he repulses you."

"I don't think that anyone can hurt me now," Salomon said somberly. "The only hurt for me would be to fail. And I don't think that I shall fail."

Since Benjamin Franklin's diplomatic triumph in Paris, which had resulted in a French treaty with America, a steady stream of French aid had been flowing across the ocean.

The French navy sailed across the Atlantic to oppose the British blockade of America. French transports carried a French army to American soil. And French money, in the form of bills of exchange and also in the form of goods, was lent to America.

Yet in spite of France's willingness, this help was woefully slow in coming. It must be remembered that

145

in those times it took a ship from forty to sixty days to cross the Atlantic Ocean from France to America. And with the powerful British navy ranging the seas and harrying the French, sometimes that time was doubled.

So the French armed forces in America did not increase too quickly, and as yet they had not participated in any major engagement. As with everything else, Philadelphia was the headquarters for these French troops, and many were quartered in the city. Others were in Rhode Island and New Jersey, but the base was at Philadelphia.

Here the French minister, Chevalier de la Luzerne, controlled the provision of those forces, and it was Luzerne whom Haym Salomon would have to see.

Salomon's first move was to buy bills. He was already acquainted with many of the French quartermasters, and now he approached them and offered them the fairest price they had had for their paper in months. This paper he endorsed and offered for resale, under his own security.

The fact that Haym Salomon had guaranteed this paper was enough to assure the coffeehouse crowd that it was as good as cash. Not that Haym Salomon's credit was better than the French government's, but France was something they did not know too well, and France was over three thousand miles away. On the other hand, they did know Haym Salomon. They knew that he had never broken his word, never let an obligation go beyond its set date, and never refused payment. If he was offering for sale bills of exchange which he himself had endorsed, that was enough for them.

146

Regardless of who won the war, Haym Salomon would pay off on the bills. It was true that he demanded a price far above that which bills of exchange commonly fetched on the general market, but those bills on the general market were not endorsed by Haym Salomon.

On the other hand, Haym Salomon did not stand to profit a great deal on his resale of the bills. He had purchased them at a high price, the highest that the market had seen in a long while, and he was selling them at exactly the same price, charging for his services interest that amounted only to one quarter of one per cent.

He was not planning to make money. He was planning to attract the attention of the French minister. If he could achieve that alone, then he would be well repaid.

In several of the Philadelphia newspapers, he inserted ads like the following:

A FEW BILLS OF EXCHANGE ON FRANCE
ST. EUSTATIA AND AMSTERDAM
TO BE SOLD BY
HAYM SALOMON, BROKER

The said Salomon will attend every day at the coffee-house between the hours of twelve and two, when he may be met with, and any kind of business in the brokerage will be undertaken by him, and those gentlemen who chuse to favor him with their business may depend upon the greatest care and punctuality.

147

His advertisements were modest, depending more upon the reputation he had made for himself than on anything he could promise in the newspapers.

His table in the corner of the coffeehouse, where he sat opposite Mr. McCrae, who always had quill and ink and ledger in front of him, had become almost the focus of attention.

The old coffeehouse, with its beamed ceilings, with its high walnut booths, was a busier hive than ever. Men rushed in and out, here and there, calling to one another, quoting prices. They rushed in, drank their coffee or hot rum, and rushed out.

Only in Haym Salomon's corner was there placid, unyielding calm. His coffee was always beside him. He drank cup after cup, to quiet his nerves and to deaden the pain in his lungs. He had come to love the feel of the place, the strong smell of freshly roasted, freshly ground coffee, the ancient grooved floors, the little windows with their frosted panes, a little knot of twisted glass in the center of each.

The coffeehouse was one of the first places he had gone to in those early Philadelphia days. He had a fatalistic feeling that the thread of his life would be spun out in this same coffeehouse.

The merchants and profiteers, remembering his penniless days, held him in almost superstitious awe, not unmixed with envy and hatred. "That Salomon," they would say, "he does mad things—he does stupid, crazy things. Yet he has a reason, you can be sure of that."

Or they would say, "Who ever heard of buying bills of

exchange, endorsing them yourself, and then selling them without profit. It's senseless, it's mad. Nobody but a Jew would do such a thing."

Yet when they attempted to beat down his price, he would look at them strangely and say:

"Gentlemen, my price is there on the front of the bill, and my name is written on the back. You can take it or leave it."

They took it. They had neither faith nor confidence in the revolution, in France, in anything except dollars and cents. But they knew that Haym Salomon had never defaulted on an obligation.

They took it, and McCrae entered the transaction in his old ledger. But sometimes he would glance up and notice a certain doubt and weariness in Salomon's eyes.

"How now, Mr. McCrae?" Salomon would ask, with more lightness than lay in his own heart. "Do you think our bait has been a little too obvious? Do you think that Luzerne saw through it, that he cares less for Jews than for financial safety?"

"He'll come to us," McCrae would answer stolidly. He, at least, had implicit faith in Salomon. "Only give him time, and he'll come to us."

"Time! Time! But there is so little time."

"How can he ignore us," McCrae would demand, "when he sees that the only French bills of exchange in Philadelphia which bring their face value are those Haym Salomon endorses?"

"I wonder," Salomon would nod thoughtfully.

149

Yet in the end Haym Salomon's plan succeeded. It happened one afternoon, as they sat in the coffeehouse. There was a stir at the door, a whispering and scurrying. The traders fell away, and the stout back of the landlord appeared, bowing violently.

"An honor," he was saying, "such an honor, your excellency. Whatever you wish, your excellency. My humble house is honored, your excellency."

McCrae twisted his long neck out of the booth and then swung back to Salomon. "It's Luzerne," he whispered. "Do you suppose—"

"I suppose nothing," Haym Salomon said calmly. "Go on with your work, Mr. McCrae."

"But Luzerne—"

"Go on with your work, Mr. McCrae."

Yet Haym Salomon could not keep the gleam of triumph out of his eyes. He had no doubt as to why Luzerne had come to the coffeehouse.

"Is Mr. Salomon here?" Luzerne asked the quivering tavernkeeper.

"Mr. Salomon. Of course, your excellency—whatever you desire, your excellency. Mr. Salomon is always here when your excellency desires to see him."

"Then lead me to him."

"Yes, your excellency."

Bowing, holding his apron and walking backward, the fat landlord led the Chevalier to Haym Salomon's booth. Luzerne wore pince-nez, and now he glanced over the lenses down at the little Jew, who rose gravely.

"Mr. Haym Salomon?" Luzerne inquired. He spoke English with some difficulty.

"Your excellency," Salomon bowed.

"I should like to talk with you."

"Gladly," Salomon nodded. "Won't you sit down?"

He motioned to the other side of the table, where a nervous Mr. McCrae hastily made room for the French minister.

"Mr. Salomon," Luzerne began, but Salomon interrupted:

"I speak French. Wouldn't you rather speak in that tongue, since this is a more or less public place?"

The minister smiled and nodded. He appreciated the diplomatic fashion in which Salomon had invited him to speak in his mother tongue.

"I love Americans and America," the minister said. "But their language, how I fear it!"

"It is difficult," Haym Salomon admitted.

"A language without rule or taste. But alas, it is too late to teach a nation of three million people to speak French."

They all laughed at that, even the dour Mr. McCrae, whose knowledge of French was almost nonexistent.

"If Mohammed will not come to the mountain," Luzerne said, "then obviously the mountain must come to Mohammed."

Salomon raised his brows. He preferred not to understand. It would be better if Luzerne made all the advances.

"I hear," Luzerne said, "that a man called Haym Salo-

151

mon is buying our bills of exchange for their face value.
I hear that he endorses them and sells them for the same
price, charging only one quarter of one per cent interest.
I am amazed—terribly amazed. My quartermasters cry
like children that no one will purchase their bills of
exchange without extorting a pound of flesh. And then,
lo and behold, a Jew called Salomon comes to the aid of
France.

"I ask myself why? Obviously not for profit, since the
profit he makes is so small that it can be disregarded. To
get in the good graces of my quartermasters? But what
can they do for Salomon? I ask my friend Robert Morris,
'Who is this Salomon?' A Jew. But I know that he is a
Jew. 'Is he honest?' I ask.

" 'I know of no more honest man,' Robert Morris tells
me, 'no one I would trust more.' 'Then why don't you
trust him?' I ask. Robert Morris says, 'He is a Jew.'

"But for me," Luzerne went on, "that is not enough.
I must see this man who is so honest. I must see this man
who trusts his country and his ally more than he trusts
English money. I must find out why he buys our bills of
exchange and endorses them when no one else will. So
I wait for him to come to me. I wait and I wait, but he
does not come. So I go to him at the coffeehouse." He
spread his hands on the table.

"I misjudged you," Salomon said. "You see, I offered
my services to Robert Morris again and again. But he
would have nothing of this upstart Polish Jew. But finally he needed me. He had to raise money quickly, and
he turned to the Jews. He turned to us on our highest

152

holy day, when we are not even allowed to think of money, yet we stopped our prayers and raised the money there on the spot. A man can stand a great deal, yet it hardens his heart when men refuse to let him serve his country because he is a Jew."

"Yet you go on trying to serve," Luzerne said keenly.

"America is all I live for," Salomon said simply.

"I see. And now as to the bills of exchange, will you explain?"

Salomon nodded eagerly. "Right now, the revolution depends upon our raising money by selling French bills of exchange. Yet your army bills, being loosely handled, have so depreciated the market that no bill will bring its face value. Now if one man were to take over all your bills, endorse them, and sell them for one price, the whole market would be steadied. It might mean our salvation."

The minister nodded thoughtfully. "I have thought of that myself. But what man would risk his good name and his fortune for a cause no businessman trusts?"

"I would," Salomon said.

The French minister eyed him keenly. "Mr. Salomon," he said, "I like to think that I am a judge of men. I don't ask where they are Jew or Christian, but whether they are true or false. From now on, the monies of the French army in America will pass through your hands. All bills of exchange will be endorsed and sold by you.

"And," he concluded, "if Robert Morris does not do likewise, he is not the man I think him to be."

Salomon could hardly speak. "I can't say how grateful I am," he whispered. "Not for myself, but for my country and yours. If America wins, she will never forget France."

"But she may forget Haym Salomon," Luzerne said thoughtfully.

A few days later, a note came from the Superintendent of Finance. It said briefly:

> *If Mr. Haym Salomon will call upon Mr. Robert Morris, tomorrow, at three o'clock, such business may be concluded which will be to their advantage and to the advantage of their country.*

CHAPTER EIGHTEEN

Robert Morris

RACHEL noticed the difference in him. Rachel had never too well understood matters of finance, nor did she try to understand the involved network her husband was weaving. It was enough for her to see that he was happy. He had accomplished something wonderful, and because he was happy, she too was happy.

He was full of energy; he vibrated with it. His cheeks, flushed by his long illness, seemed now to take on the ruddiness of real health. His long brown eyes sparkled with eagerness.

He was dressing, and as he dressed, he laughed and chatted, pausing every now and then to kiss her.

"Something I had almost forgotten," he explained.

"I was beginning to wonder whether I still had a husband—or only a financial machine." She fastened the fresh, starched ruff onto his shirt front.

"My black coat," he said. "The black one with the velvet lapels."

"The Superintendent of Finance will think you a dandy, instead of a sober businessman."

"Will he? I don't know. Anyway, I must look my best. How would I feel attending Robert Morris in the old brown broadcloth, smelling as it does of a hundred days in the coffeehouse?"

"Of course," Rachel nodded. Nothing was too wonderful for her husband. She had heard the story of how the great Chevalier de la Luzerne himself had sought out Haym Salomon in his corner of the coffeehouse.

She tied his hair carefully into the pigtail and set the cocked hat upon his head.

"Am I all right?" he asked eagerly.

"Very handsome," she smiled.

"But nervous," he said. "I can't let him see that I am nervous."

"I can't see it myself," she assured him.

Yet there were tears in her eyes as she stood at the door and watched him walk jauntily away, as if he hadn't a care in the world.

At Morris's house, he was kept waiting in the anteroom for almost an hour. During that hour, his nervousness increased. Fears and doubts began to plague him. Had Morris changed his mind? Had he decided in the end that he did not want to depend upon a Jew, regardless of how necessary that Jew was to him? Was he preparing, even now, to send Salomon away without even speaking to him?

He turned his hat over and over in his hands. He stared at the gloomy paintings that lined the walls. It was said that Robert Morris was a hard man, a violent man, an impatient and intolerant man.

Yet why should he, who knew only too well the lies men speak of those they envy, believe what was said about Morris? Wasn't he the first, when hearing of Morris's appointment to the Treasury, to exult? Hadn't he sincerely believed that Morris would save America?

He put his doubts out of mind. Regardless of what attitude Robert Morris took, it would make no difference. If he, Haym Salomon, could not carry on his work with Morris, then he would find some way to carry on without him.

At that moment, a clerk came out and said that the Superintendent of Finance would see Mr. Salomon.

Robert Morris was, at that time, a man past middle age, stout, careless in dress, impatient in manners and speech. He had a square face, a long nose, a broad, blunt chin, and a heavy neck. When he spoke, he took no pains to hide his thoughts in the little courtesies of the day.

As Salomon entered the office, he didn't rise, but simply nodded from where he sat behind a paper-littered table. "Mr. Haym Salomon," he said.

Salomon bowed, stood before the table uneasily.

"Sit down." Morris motioned to a chair.

After Salomon had seated himself, Morris stared

thoughtfully at the table. Still not looking at Haym Salomon, he said bluntly:

"The Chevalier de la Luzerne advised me to see you. He also advised me that he was placing in your hands all bills of exchange issued to the French army in America. I intimated that I considered this a somewhat dangerous thing to do, but he said that he did not think so at all.

"Now what is your purpose in cornering those bills of exchange? If you guaranteed a price to Luzerne, then you stand to make no profit worth mentioning."

"I didn't do it for profit," Haym Salomon answered quietly.

"Then what were your motives?"

"You didn't ask for motives," Haym Salomon said, "when you sent to the synagogue for money on Yom Kippur."

Morris hesitated between anger and uncertainty. Finally he said, "I didn't know it was your holy day. I don't know that much about Jews."

Salomon nodded. "Then I apologize," he said simply.

"And as to the bills of exchange?"

"They were breaking the market. You know that as well as I do. You depend upon bills of exchange to keep the armies in the field, and unless you can sell those bills for a fair price, your cause is hopeless. And you can't sell them."

"Who said I can't?" Morris roared.

"It's common knowledge in Philadelphia. Also," Salomon said bluntly, "you would not have turned to the Jews

158

that day if you could have found the money anywhere else."

Morris started to his feet, his eyes blazing; then he sank back into his chair. He stared at Salomon a moment and smiled.

"You're an outspoken man, Mr. Salomon," he said.

"There's no other way. You don't like Jews. That doesn't matter to me. But one thing we are both sincerely concerned with—and that is winning this war. Suppose we both lay aside our animosity. I can help you with what you're trying to do. Will you let me help you?"

"Explain yourself."

"For one thing," Salomon began, "I intend to endorse all bills of exchange that pass through my hands. I intend to keep the price up. Once I have stabilized the market, I will be able to turn into cash any and all bills of exchange you care to entrust to me. Regardless of when you need money, I will find it for you. That's my solemn pledge."

"And what makes you think your credit is good enough to bear that weight?"

"I have never defaulted. I'm not boasting when I say that no banker in Philadelphia will refuse to accept my endorsement."

Morris nodded. Then his eyes narrowed. "What will be your interest charges?" he demanded.

"Charges? I made no mention of charges," Haym Salomon said.

Morris shook his head. "If we do business, we do it upon a sound basis. Two per cent is the current rate."

159

Still Salomon shook his head.

"Either you are that rare thing, a patriotic businessman, or else you are insane," Morris said.

"Perhaps I am insane."

"That may be. Still you must set some price on your services. A matter like this can take all and more than all of a man's time."

"Well then," Salomon considered, "let it be one quarter of one per cent. That will suffice."

"Very well," Morris agreed. He sat back, his eyes closed for a moment, and then he said bluntly:

"I'm going to trust you, Salomon. Perhaps I'm a fool for trusting you, yet money will be needed. All the money we can lay hands on. Within the week, I'm leaving for the North—to see General Washington. What will come of that meeting, even I don't know. But it will be something big. That's no secret—everyone knows that now, if ever, is the time to strike. But whatever it is, we'll need money, more money, and more money.

"My assistant, Gouverneur Morris, will be in charge here while I'm gone. I'll instruct him to call upon you whenever he needs cash. And rest assured, he will need it."

"I won't fail you," Salomon said.

CHAPTER NINETEEN

ANUMBER of circumstances had led up to the series of events that started with Robert Morris's journey to see General Washington.

Several years had passed since that day Haym Salomon arrived in Philadelphia, shortly after the British had evacuated the city. As told before, George Washington and his veterans of the winter at Valley Forge had fallen upon the British column as it wound through the Jersey lowlands, and there, at Monmouth, the first really decisive victory of the war was won by the Americans.

Yet that victory did not bring the war to an end. So greatly were the Americans outnumbered by the British that Washington never again had occasion to risk a decisive battle with the superior British army.

Weeks and months and years passed, and still the war went on its painful, bitter course. There were small battles, skirmishes, attacks and counterattacks, but no battle

161

which might inflict a decisive defeat upon one side or
the other.

Meanwhile, in Paris, Benjamin Franklin had scored
a major diplomatic victory. France committed herself
to an alliance with America, and French troops began to
arrive on American soil. Yet even these new reinforce-
ments could not alter the balance of power. The British
army, at that time, was the finest army in the world, and
it was backed by all the strength and prestige of the
British Empire and the British fleet.

If the French fleet had been powerful enough to risk
an engagement with the British fleet and defeat the British fleet, then the lines of communication between the
Old World and the New might have been cut, and
thereby Britain might have been defeated. But Britain
ruled the seas, and the French fleet was not to dispute
that rule until about thirty years later, when Nelson
swept the French from the seas at Trafalgar.

Yet even had the British fleet been defeated, it is not
certain that the war would have come to an end. For in
the thirteen states, thousands of people sided with the
British. As its name implies, the revolution was every
bit as much of a civil war as a war against a foreign
power.

During the years that Salomon labored in Philadelphia
to build up some sort of financial force which might aid
his country, the fortunes of free America were sinking
lower and lower. Though the British could not defeat
the Americans, the Americans were nevertheless being

162

defeated. They were being defeated in what was for them a superhuman task—the task of keeping two armies in the field at the same time.

The British in America were divided into two main forces. There was the northern army, based at New York City; and there was the southern army, more mobile, commanded by Lord Cornwallis. To oppose these, the Americans had to keep two armies operating simultaneously. And this had to be done by a Congress which had no power to tax.

As Salomon had foreseen, the one dread enemy America could not defeat was bankruptcy.

Each winter that passed was worse, and each winter that approached was more dreaded. For during the winter, the armies would have to encamp. Food would grow scarce, and winter clothes would have to be found. Through the long months of idleness, the men would grow homesick and restive. They would demand pay that could not be found. They would mutiny. They would desert by the hundreds.

Only one force kept the army together during those terrible winters—the dogged, driving power of George Washington. And even he dreaded what would happen during this coming winter of 1781-1782. He knew that a move had to be made, some move, any move. He also knew that victory or defeat now would spell victory or defeat in the final outcome of the war.

And that was why, in August 1781, he sent for Robert Morris.

163

Now let us see exactly what George Washington had in mind when he sent out to Philadelphia that desperate summons for Robert Morris. You remember that Haym Salomon fled from a New York which was in British hands. You also remember that in 1776 the Continental Army had fled that same New York.

For five years New York had been the prize of the British, and for five years George Washington had a bitter memory of the succession of defeats that had marked his New York campaign: Long Island, Brooklyn Heights, Harlem Heights. He never forgot those defeats, and he never gave up his hope of recapturing New York from the British.

Now, in 1781, his army was camped in Westchester County. American headquarters were still at Dobbs Ferry, a few miles up the Hudson River from the northern tip of Manhattan Island, just where they had been three years before, when Haym Salomon fled from New York. And George Washington still brooded over his dream of capturing New York.

A part of the French army was camped at Newport, Rhode Island. Washington communicated with Rochambeau, who was in command of the French forces, and begged him to assist in an attack upon New York. Rochambeau agreed. But even when both armies were combined, the French and the Americans, they could muster no more than seven thousand men.

Washington and Rochambeau surveyed the defenses of New York. The story goes that they rode south, through the no man's land, to the banks of Spuyten

164

SON OF LIBERTY

Duyvil itself. That they drove their horses along the edge
of the palisades. That they stood in a small boat, sailing
close to the shores of Manhattan.

And everywhere they saw the same thing, impregnable
defenses, bristling batteries of field guns, massed ranks
of Hessians, earthworks, breastworks, defenses of every
type and fashion.

Washington realized the futility of attempting to capture New York with his seven thousand men. So did
Rochambeau. Sir Henry Clinton, in command of the
British, had stuffed the city with Redcoats and Hessians.
The British fleet, with its towering banks of guns, lay
in the harbor, ready to sail around the city and belch its
iron death at any attempt the Americans made. Washington saw that there was only one hope of taking New
York: more men and a fleet to oppose the British fleet.

At that time, the French fleet, under the command of
Admiral de Grasse, lay at the West Indies. Washington
sent him an urgent plea to come and join in an attack
upon New York. The great French fleet, which included
three thousand troops, could have turned the tide in
Washington's favor. The British in New York, the largest British army in America, could then be surrounded
and forced to surrender. And with their surrender would
come the end of the war.

De Grasse agreed to sail to America with his fleet.
But he would come as far as Chesapeake Bay, no farther
—as he dared not get too far from his base in the West
Indies.

That was the last blow. With that news, Washington

167

saw his whole beloved plan crumble to pieces. In a fit of awful despair, he sent for Robert Morris.

But by the time Morris had arrived, a new plan had come into being. Perhaps it was a relief for Washington to realize that New York must be rejected from his plans, for he threw himself into his new idea, the master stroke of the war.

He would take his whole army of seven thousand men, march them five hundred miles to the south, and join General Greene in one great blow against the forces of Cornwallis.

The plan was so tremendous, so brilliant, that it overshadowed all his disappointments. He threw himself into it. He set to work and constructed on the palisades overlooking New York earthworks and artillery emplacements. The British must believe that he was going on with his plans to take New York.

And meanwhile he waited eagerly for Robert Morris.

Finally Morris arrived. Washington held a conference. He outlined carefully to all those present his great plan for an attack upon Cornwallis in the South. When he had finished, he turned to Richard Peters, secretary of the board of war.

"What can you do for me?" Washington asked him.

"With money, everything. Without money—nothing."

A silence fell over the group. One by one, they fixed their eyes upon Robert Morris. And still he sat silent, with all of them awaiting his reply.

Perhaps there ran through his mind then a picture of

the complex financial whirl of Philadelphia. Perhaps he saw the coffeehouses, the hoarse, shouting traders. Perhaps he recalled a small, brown-eyed Jew, who had promised never to fail him.

"Let me know how much you want," Robert Morris said calmly.

A sigh of relief ran through the assemblage. They bent their heads, figured costs, made estimates.

In the end, Robert Morris borrowed from Rochambeau the twenty thousand dollars requested. He did not know how he would pay back the money. There was only one source, and he wondered whether Haym Salomon would fail him or not.

CHAPTER TWENTY

MEANWHILE, in Philadelphia, that other portion of the war went on, that grim, silent
struggle to conjure money out of nowhere.
Men had to be fed, men had to be paid, men had to be
clothed—that was a perpetual cycle.

Haym Salomon had never realized what enormous
amounts of food an army can consume, even such a small
army as the American one. Even an army that was used to
half rations. The main army, under Washington, was
in Westchester County, but regiments and battalions
were scattered all over the country. And they all had to
eat. And they all had to walk upon shoe leather, not on
their bare soles.

The requests for food and pay were endless. The problem was never settled. Once a member of Congress con-
ceived a brilliant idea—to empower General Washington

to seize flour whenever he needed it. But there was still enough sanity left to keep a revolutionary army from turning into a bandit force.

At that time, Robert Morris bought two thousand barrels of flour on his own credit. So for the moment the situation was saved. But only for the moment. The borrowing process went on. Washington had spent his last penny. So had Morris. So had a hundred other men. So had Haym Salomon.

Sometimes he marked down loans, sometimes he didn't. Fifty dollars would buy a member of Congress a suit of clothes and a dozen square meals. The dollars came from Haym Salomon. This regiment needed cornmeal. Haym Salomon would collar a Jewish merchant in the synagogue, and soon a hundred barrels of cornmeal would be on their way.

A corporal who had fought two years in the Pennsylvania line under Anthony Wayne, who had had his arm shot away at Stony Point, walked the streets of Philadelphia. A pension from Haym Salomon kept him alive.

Shall a good revolutionist starve? Haggard, war-worn men, their lank hair brushing against bearded cheeks, knew that the coffeehouse was their one refuge. It was pay and pay and pay—

Sometimes, Mr. McCrae would warn him, "There will soon be nothing, Mr. Salomon, nothing left."

Yet there always was something. A ship would run the blockade, and the profits would be high. Or a privateer would come into port, bulging with loot. Somehow

171

his money lasted. Somehow he was able to earn more money, to keep ahead of the incessant demands.

All this was aside from his main purpose, which was to sell bills of exchange and raise the money Congress needed so urgently. Hour after hour he sat in his booth in the coffeehouse, a cup of steaming hot brew next to him, Mr. McCrae across from him, making notations in the old ledger.

He was no longer unknown. The market of wildcat prices in bills of exchange had been broken, and Haym Salomon had broken it. He sold government paper for a price it had never fetched before, and as a result of that a steady stream of money poured into the Treasury.

But he had made enemies. How can a man become rich in Philadelphia when this Jew will not allow usury? The Tories lost no chance to insult him, and their insults were not veiled.

For all that, though again and again anger blazed in his brown eyes, he never lost his calm sense of balance. He was still the shy little man, the courteous little man. Even his firmness was never rude. When the jostling crowd of brokers around his table attempted to beat down the price, he would merely smile at them and say:

"Gentlemen, if you will not buy at my price, then I must close down my stall. Business for the day is over."

And then he would leave them to fume and threaten.

But it was not only the Tories he had to contend with. Gouverneur Morris, who was in charge during the absence of Robert Morris, did not spare Salomon. He resented the fact that a Jew should perform such a necessary service, and he resented the confidence Robert Morris had placed in Haym Salomon.

If he could find any fault, real or imaginary, in the way money was obtained, he scored Salomon roundly. He never let Haym Salomon forget that regardless of what he might do, he was still a Jew and a broker—and no more.

His demands for money were incessant, highhanded, urgent, and his complaints flowed in a never-ending stream. France was giving America more financial help than ever now. The loans from France were mounting up into tens of thousands of dollars. But those loans were still in the form of bills of exchange, and for every bill Haym Salomon had to find cash somewhere.

Often it was at the synagogue. The prayer would be over, and then Haym Salomon would call the Jews around him. As soon as they saw him unfolding the bills of exchange from his capacious wallet, they knew what would follow.

"This Salomon," they would murmur, "he is like a well gone dry. Pour water into it from now until Judgment Day and still it will ask for more."

Salomon would unfold the papers and say, "Gentlemen, there are a few bills here that the wolves at the coffeehouse refused to take down their maw. Perhaps the risk is none too good. Rumor has it that General Washington will attack New York, and the best opinion of those

173

military experts who do their fighting over beer in the Philadelphia taverns is that the general will fail. So you see, gentlemen, the risk is none too good. The coffeehouse crowd refused me."

That was his way of flattering them—to come to them with bills of exchange he could sell nowhere else and to tell them he could sell them nowhere else.

"But Salomon, you have milked us dry."

He would merely raise his brows to that.

"But where is the end, Salomon? One day it is a thousand dollars, ten thousand dollars the next day, a thousand dollars again."

"The end? When the war is over."

"But we are in debt already—"

"Then go further into debt," Salomon would say brutally. "For two thousand years the Jews have been praying for a return to their promised land. I say that promised land is here—in America."

"But Salomon—"

"I have five bills, gentlemen, a thousand dollars apiece. The money is needed desperately."

In the end they would raise the money for him, and flour would be bought and blankets would be bought, and the foundering ship of state would sail on a while longer.

It was a business of manning the pumps and pumping without respite. The leaks were not stopped. On the military front, a battle might be won or lost. But here the struggle for money had no high spots. It was a process of scraping the bottom and always finding a little more.

But there were times when even he succumbed to doubt, when he lay awake all night, smothering his hollow cough, wondering what would be the end of all this.

Was it true that Washington would attack New York with his pitifully inferior forces? Was it true that he would fail? Was it true that the revolution would sprawl out and die a death of exhaustion?

But always, the next day, in the battle of wits, in the battle of the coffeehouse, in the battle of the trade marts, he would come intensely alive again. Coming home, he would say to Rachel:

"Another day, and she's still afloat."

He would kiss her, and she would be terribly proud of him, even though she was hopelessly confused by the complications of his work. Yet if it brought him happiness, wasn't that enough?

He would relate to her whatever stories of the day might interest her. For instance, how a Quaker by the name of Barnaby had two thousand blankets the government needed. The Quaker had asked three dollars a blanket.

"Can you imagine, Rachel?" he would storm, furious suddenly. "Six thousand dollars—two hundred per cent profit for him while men lie in the cold and freeze. I said to him, 'Mr. Barnaby, take your profit, but before God, I'll ruin you.'

"He wanted to know how. I told him I'd spread lies about him—I told him I'd undermine his business, his reputation. I put the fear of God into him."

"But was that right?"

"Right? I don't know. All I know is that he sold the blankets for a dollar apiece, and that two thousand men will be warm. That's all that matters."

In moments like that he frightened her. What was happening to this gentle husband of hers? She would never understand that he was at war, that the only rule he lived by was victory for the cause he believed in.

Robert Morris had returned to Philadelphia. He was back in the city only one day when he summoned Haym Salomon.

Salomon related briefly the conditions of the Philadelphia market. "They believe that Washington will attack New York," he concluded. "And they believe that he will fail. Money is very difficult to find."

That careful understatement brought the first smile in many a day to the face of the Superintendent of Finance.

"Mr. Salomon," he said, "General Washington does not attack New York."

Haym Salomon waited.

"No—the rest is a military secret for the time being. Only be assured that something will happen. Also be assured that regardless of what happens, it will make it no easier for us to go on. Money is needed more now than ever."

Salomon shook his head.

"I am twenty thousand dollars in debt to Rochambeau," Morris said. "Bills have come to cover that amount, but the bills must be sold. The money must be found—somewhere."

176

"I'll try," Salomon said.

He tried. Sometimes it seemed to him that he was living in a nightmare. Money and more money and more money.

Money for medicine, for food, for arms.

Money to pay the members of Congress, to pay officers and enlisted men, to pay clerks.

Money for blankets, for clothes, for shoes.

Money to pay interest on loans, to pay loans due.

Money to buy horses, to buy saddles.

Loans and more loans and more loans.

It seemed to him sometimes that the whole world was pauperized and crying aloud for money on which to exist.

He needed more and more coffee to keep up his strength as he sat opposite Mr. McCrae. He was even losing his calm. His voice grew hoarse and ragged as he tried to shout down the rapacious brokers.

His demands on the synagogue became more frequent. When other sources failed, he went to the Jews. Yet there were only a few Jews in Philadelphia.

He spoke to wandering Jewish peddlers, and soon his importunate demands for money were threading their way up and down the country. Wherever there were Jews, the quiet voice of Haym Salomon was heard.

Give.

Give more.

And still more.

There was no comfort to be gained from Robert Morris. He was a battered man. For every demand upon

Haym Salomon, there were two upon Robert Morris.

It began to tell upon Haym Salomon. The cough he had gotten in the damp cell of the Provost Jail grew worse. And then one day he fainted in the coffeehouse.

A white-faced Rachel saw McCrae bring the little man into the house. Trembling and tearful, she waited by his bedside for the doctor.

But there was little comfort to be gained from the doctor. "He must rest," the doctor said. "I told him that before."

"Yes, yes, he'll rest," Rachel whispered.

When Salomon opened his eyes at last, Rachel kissed him and said, "It's all right, darling. Everything will be all right."

He nodded weakly. "Where is McCrae?" he whispered.

McCrae stood by the bed, his dour face tensely anxious.

"McCrae," Salomon said. "Go back to the coffeehouse. Keep up the price and make them buy."

CHAPTER TWENTY-ONE

NOW the great drama of the war of independence got under way, and Haym Salomon, sick, worn down fine by his efforts, was unable to see or know it.

Washington put all his heart into making the great encampment on the palisades as convincing as possible. Each day, British officers walked along the waterfront, where Riverside Drive is today, and stared through spyglasses at the Jersey shore. There, on top of the palisades, they saw a great commotion of men at work, and many things being done. During the day, they saw trees toppling over, ditches being dug, cannon wheeled into position.

The British officers smiled to themselves and said, "Good, good, the old fox is digging his grave. When he attacks, we'll beat him back to his hole in the ground,

179

and then flank him. Then we'll smoke him out, and this whole deadly nuisance of a war will be over."

At night, great campfires blazed on top of the cliff. The British officers toasted one another at this final stupidity of the rebel commander. They knew he could have no more than seven thousand men. They knew his attack on New York would fail.

But just to be sure, just to take no chances, Sir Henry Clinton sent a messenger to Cornwallis. He told Cornwallis to stay close to the sea, and if he needed him, he would send for him.

Then the British settled down comfortably to await the attack and the final defeat of these rebels.

The attack never came. One dark night, Washington set his whole ponderous force of seven thousand men in motion. But not to attack New York. Instead, they crossed the Hudson River and set out under forced march toward Philadelphia. All night they marched, and all night the fires burned on the palisades.

And in the morning, when the British awoke, there was still activity in the spurious American encampment. The British sat back and smiled.

Not until the American-French army was far beyond reach in the dusty Jersey lowlands did Sir Henry Clinton suddenly come to his senses. He noticed that the American earthworks across the Hudson were very quiet of late, and he sent over some spies to investigate. The spies came back and told him that the whole encampment was a fake, that the Americans were nowhere in the vicinity, but had last been seen marching south at full speed.

Sir Henry Clinton shrugged his shoulders. The old fox had evidently lost his nerve. Perhaps it occurred to him that Washington was marching south to attack Cornwallis, but if it did, he evidently counted on Cornwallis to take care of himself. After all, American troops were not something to really fear, he thought.

And meanwhile, Washington's seven thousand men rolled on toward Philadelphia. Clouds of dry dust sifted across the countryside, and farmers paused in their work to watch the long lines of battered Continentals march past.

The tune of Yankee Doodle lingered in their ears, and the same tune cleared the ears of Philadelphia citizens as Washington and his men reached the city.

It was a great occasion when they entered the city. That they were going south to trap Cornwallis was no longer a military secret, and the whole town buzzed with talk of the anticipated victory. The people lined the streets, packed shoulder to shoulder, to catch a glimpse of the famous general and his war-weary veterans.

They cheered and screamed as the Continentals marched past. What a day, what a great day! How simple things were, and how simple it was to carry through a war and win it. Just stand and cheer and tell your neighbor that you knew all along it would come out this way, that the old fox would pull the wool over Sir Henry Clinton's eyes.

Yes, rumor had it that already young Lafayette had pushed Cornwallis back into a safe place, and was now only waiting for Washington to come and dig the British out.

And they had known all the time—it was so simple.

That evening, the members of Congress gave a great banquet at the City Tavern. The banquet was in honor of the French officers who were marching with Washington, and everyone who mattered in the city was there. It was something to be remembered and discussed over and over again in Philadelphia drawing rooms for the next twenty years.

Robert Morris was there, sitting near Washington, but it is doubtful whether even he wasted much time thinking of a small brown-eyed broker who was not there and whom nobody missed.

Perhaps the Chevalier de la Luzerne, resplendent in silk and brocade and lace recalled the small Jew with the hacking cough. But it is doubtful whether many others did.

In his bed, Haym Salomon heard them cheering, heard the stamp of thousands of marching feet. He asked Rachel:

"What is it? What is it?"

"The army is here. They marched from New York."

"They are going south?" Haym Salomon whispered.

"Yes, but don't think of that now. Rest now. You have to rest. The doctor said so."

182

"South to attack Cornwallis," Salomon murmured. "If it succeeds, it may mean everything."

"Please rest," Rachel begged him.

That night, while the great banquet went on in the City Tavern, Haym Salomon tossed in feverish slumber.

And McCrae sat by his bed, trying to understand why a man should give all for something which yielded neither glory nor honor.

The army did not linger long in Philadelphia. They were off for the South, and by stages they reached York-town, where Cornwallis had dug himself in.

Meanwhile, from the West Indies, De Grasse's fleet had arrived and closed the final path of escape for Cornwallis, the sea. All of the major forces in America had joined one another now, and for the first time in his life, Washington found himself in command of forty thousand men—thirty-one thousand French soldiers and about nine thousand of his own Continentals.

What happened at Yorktown has been told elsewhere. It is sufficient to note that the Americans and the French ringed in the British, tightened their lines, and then attacked.

There was no escape for either Cornwallis or his men. At two o'clock, Friday afternoon, October 19, 1781, the great British army surrendered. That was after six years of war.

Haym Salomon was still in bed when the news arrived in Philadelphia. McCrae brought it to him. And as the dour Scotsman told Haym Salomon the story of the surrender of the British army, the little man's eyes burned with joy.

"We've won!" he cried. "McCrae, it's not the end yet, but we've won! Do you understand?"

"Ay, it's good news," McCrae nodded.

"Good news? It's victory, do you understand? Real victory—the first real victory of the war." He threw back the covers and stumbled out of bed.

"McCrae, help me to dress."

"Where are you going?" McCrae demanded. "You're a sick man."

"Not any more. Help me to dress, McCrae. I must go down to the coffeehouse. I must sit there and let those who laughed and sneered at me know that I lived to see a British army surrender."

He left the house on McCrae's arm, and still leaning on McCrae's arm, he entered the coffeehouse. But for all his weakness, his face was alight with triumph.

184

IT DID not matter to Haym Salomon that he was still weak, that the doctor solemnly warned him, that his family and friends pleaded with him. He was soon back in his old place at the coffeehouse.

He told his friends, "When great things are being done, how can I lie at home like a log?"

Indeed, he felt that he had been born again, once he was out of bed and back in the streets. He loved the old town of Philadelphia. He had come to have a greater affection for it than he had ever owned for the British-dominated New York. He felt that here was the place in America that had become truly his, the little squares, the narrow streets, and the old red Quaker houses.

As soon as he was able to, he walked down to the

waterfront. It had never lost its power to thrill him, this part of the city which he had seen first. The great piles of merchandise represented that section of life which he knew best. The heaped bales of cotton, the hogsheads of tobacco, the baskets of fresh-carded wool, the tin boxes of spices that had traveled across half the world, the iron ingots, the copper bars, the roped piles of stiff, untanned hides, the barrels of flour, the bales of fur.

Incoming and outgoing, it was the blood of America, the nation's commerce. He knew that after the war the tide of merchandise would swell to inconceivable proportions, and he wondered wistfully whether his strength would hold out long enough for him to see some of that boom. Not forever would commerce be carried on in the coffeehouse; there would be banks and great houses of exchange.

The privateers and blockade runners recognized him and welcomed him eagerly. A long time had passed since he visited the docks, what with the feverish days of selling and then his illness. Captains and owners shook his hand and pointed out changes in the vast fleet that now filled the port.

"The *Jenny Bry* there," they told him. "She ran from a British frigate eighteen days. Never could lose her and never let her get within gunshot. And loaded to the gills with coffee—sixteen thousand dollars' worth."

It gave him a feeling of envy and frustration to know that such wealth existed while his pauperized government pleaded for dollars and pennies.

"And that brig there?" he asked.

"The *Maryland*—a privateer. She fought it out running with a frigate, knocked over a mast and left her cooling her heels. You can still see the scars on her."

A leathery-brown old captain told him how they had slipped through the British patrol at Gibraltar one dark night. "So close that they saw us," he laughed. "Thought we were one of them and yelled, 'Keep a sharp eye for Yankees!' Well, we did."

Haym Salomon found some old friends of the synagogue fitting out a privateer for an adventure to the Indies. She would be ready to sail in a day or two, but out of eight shares in her, two were still unsold.

"Come in on her, Salomon," they said. "She's as neat a craft of twenty-two guns as you ever laid eyes on. Marcus Yasudi is supercargo on her, and there's no better eye in the world for guessing whether a British East Indiaman sails empty or with a fat cargo of treasure under her decks."

"She'll leave a path of broken timber through the British fleet," another added, "and she'll come back with a five hundred per cent profit."

"When?" Salomon asked.

"Eighteen months."

He bought the remaining two shares, but he shook his head. Eighteen months was a long time. It was now that money was needed.

His friends laughed and said: "Cheer up, Salomon. In a year and a half, you'll still be plaguing with your eternal bills of exchange."

The surrender of Cornwallis at Yorktown was a great victory for the armed forces, but for that little group who fought their silent battle against the specter of bankruptcy it meant a good deal less.

For in spite of the fact that Yorktown broke the back of the British effort in America, it did not bring peace. In fact, two long, hard years were to roll by before a peace treaty was signed. And during those two years, the army had to be maintained.

After the Battle of Yorktown and the American victory, Admiral de Grasse put his men on board ship again and sailed with his fleet to the protection of the French West Indies. There he encountered the British fleet, and there a stunning defeat was inflicted upon the French. De Grasse's fleet was battered into splinters, the greatest part of it destroyed, and three thousand men lost.

The British lion knew how to bite, in spite of the fact that he had lost an army.

But in London, the people were fed up with the war. When they heard of the surrender of Cornwallis, they rose in arms against the continuance of the war.

"Enough!" they screamed to Parliament. "How long must we feed you our sons? Six years is enough!"

In Parliament, there had always been a faction against war with America, and now a bitter struggle raged. The British armies were being defeated upon both sides of the ocean. Only the King and the Tories were left to defend them and to carry on the war. And their effort was small.

But in America, it was known only that while one English army had surrendered, another remained firmly entrenched in New York. And through the South there were Tory factions still carrying on the struggle. Also there were British garrisons in Savannah and Charleston.

The war had to go on. Anthony Wayne led his men against the British in the South, and Washington took his army to Newburgh, where he might be ready for any fresh move of the British from Canada and where he might keep an anxious eye upon New York.

He took his army—and winter was coming. Thus it began again, the old, old tale dinned into the silent men at Philadelphia.

Money to pay the men.

Clothes for the winter, food, arms.

And more and still more.

It would be interesting here to show how little Yorktown altered the financial situation, to quote from Robert Morris's diary.

The first entry is dated October 24, 1781, as follows·

> This morning Colo. Tilghman arrived with dispatches from His Excellency Genl Washington giving account of the surrender of Earl Cornwallis and his army at York in Virginia to the combined forces under his Excellency's command. Sent for Mr. Kinnan the Copper Plater Printer who thinks his Salary insufficient.

And the very next day, October 25, Robert Morris has this to say:

Begins as usual with Applications for Money. Mr. Parker of the Loan Office of South Carolina called and informed that the papers of the Office are at Hagers Town in Maryland, and that he has not Money to defray his expenses of bringing them hither &c &c.

It was plain enough that the surrender at Yorktown, while the best of news, made little change in the lives of men who lived in a nightmare of demands for money.

So again Robert Morris sent for Haym Salomon. He sent for the one man who never refused him, never bickered with him, never demanded money, never demanded anything.

"Sit down," he nodded at Salomon. His attitude toward the little man had changed. He had found a person he could trust. He had found a person utterly without ambition for himself, a person whose only desire was to serve.

And more than anything else, he had found a man whose word was never broken. Sometimes he wondered whether if he asked for a moon on a silver platter Haym Salomon would bring it to him.

"It was a great victory," Robert Morris said, and then in the next breath added, "But it doesn't change things. We are still penniless. No one has money—for anything, and they all come to me."

"I know," Haym Salomon nodded. He didn't think it necessary to add that many of them came to Haym Salo-

190

mon for money after they had failed to break through the granite surface of the Superintendent of Finance.

"There are no signs of a peace treaty. The army has to be kept together."

"I know," Haym Salomon said calmly.

"It means money. I don't know from where—I don't know how, but we have to have money."

Again Haym Salomon nodded.

"I've thought of one thing," Robert Morris said. "We have to raise the price on bills of exchange."

Haym Salomon stared at him. "There are some things that even I can't do," he protested.

"But you must. We must make them six shillings threepence. At least that will buy a thousand loaves of bread here, a thousand coats there."

Now these bills of exchange, issued by French banks, were marked in livres, the unit of French money. They had to be sold for Pennsylvania or British money, which was figured in shillings. They could not be turned into American dollars, because American dollars were worthless and would buy nothing.

Haym Salomon had been selling the bills at the rate of five and a half shillings for five livres. Five livres amounted roughly to what a dollar would have been worth had American currency been sound.

And even at that price, it was only by sweat and tears that Haym Salomon found customers for his bills. Now, if the price were raised, how would he find any money at all?

191

"You're asking the impossible," Haym Salomon said.

"I'm asking what I must. The victory at Yorktown should have changed the attitude of the people. They should be more willing to buy."

"They should—but they're not."

"Still, Mr. Salomon, the bills must be sold at the new price."

"Very well," Haym Salomon said. "I'll try."

Robert Morris smiled. He knew that when Haym Salomon tried, he did not fail.

It was a weary Haym Salomon who came into the office at Front Street and faced Mr. McCrae.

"And what did Morris say?" McCrae demanded. "Or was he so bewildered at one person who was not deviling him for a loan that he could say nothing at all?"

"He said that I must raise the price on bills of exchange to six shillings threepence."

"He said that?"

Haym Salomon smiled at the Scotsman's wonder.

"Did he say how?" the Scotsman asked with a sardonic smile.

"He didn't seem to think it so unusual."

"No—and he never thinks it unusual to ask the impossible of Haym Salomon."

"He doesn't want the money for himself," Haym Salomon said. "The army has to eat—"

"And what thanks will be yours for this?"

"I don't ask for thanks. Let others have the glory."

"But how will we sell them?" McCrae demanded.

"How? Who will buy? Where will the money come from?"

"I don't know," Salomon said tiredly. "I don't know at all. It will come from somewhere, I suppose. It always has come from somewhere. Only sometimes I'm weary, terribly weary. I wonder whether there will ever be an end of it."

"You're my employer," McCrae said angrily, "and we've been together many years. But sometimes I find it hard to keep from calling you a fool."

Haym Salomon shook his head. "I wanted to serve. This is the only way I know. Come, we'll go to the coffee-house now."

The coffeehouse was crowded. The victory at York-town had caused a flurry of trading, and prices on several key commodities were falling. This was because the British fleet had not disputed Admiral de Grasse's command of the sea.

The brokers decided that this meant control of the seas had been wrested from the British. Otherwise, why hadn't Sir Henry Clinton come to Cornwallis's aid? And if British control had been broken, then it would no longer be necessary to run the blockade to bring food and other goods into America.

This speculation that the British blockade of the American coast was over and done with caused what is known in financial circles as a falling market. It meant that while an almost overwhelming majority of traders was eager to sell, almost no one was willing to buy.

Many of the coffeehouse profiteers had invested heavily in key goods, such as woolen cloth, flour, leather, iron, lead, all those things necessary to the carrying on of the war. These men, who cared little for either the revolutionary or the British cause, cornered such commodities and held them for a rise in price.

Now thinking that a stream of such materials would flow into the country soon, they were anxious to sell. And as with any market where everyone is eager to sell and no one to buy, prices kept dropping fantastically.

That was the scene which presented itself to Salomon when he entered the coffeehouse. He took his place, but no one was interested in bills of exchange. When they heard of the rise in price, they laughed at him.

"We can't sell today," McCrae sighed.

"If that falling market isn't stopped, we won't be able to sell for a month," Salomon said desperately.

"And how do you intend to stop it?"

"Buy—buy everything they offer. They're fools if they think the British blockade is over."

"We can't buy," McCrae protested. "We have no money."

"My word's good. We'll pay next month—or in sixty days. Only buy and stop that selling."

"It's suicide," McCrae murmured.

"I don't care what it is. Buy."

McCrae started to buy. He bought desperately, with the attitude of a man who is plunging over the edge of a thousand-foot cliff. He bought until the price had stopped falling, until it began very slowly to rise again.

194

The traders said, "He's Haym Salomon's man, and you can be sure he's behind this. See how calmly he sits there, never even bending an ear to falling prices. You can be sure he knows what he's doing. You can be sure he has inside information of some kind."

They drifted over to Haym Salomon's table. He said, with assurance he in no way felt:

"Gentlemen, this is a time to buy. And there are no better securities than these French loans, these bills of exchange drawn upon the safest banks in France."

"You're asking a fantastic price, Salomon."

"Am I? And tomorrow they'll be selling sixpence higher. Buy, gentlemen, buy."

They bought. Salomon endorsed each note, watching with an anxious eye as hundreds and thousands of dollars mounted before him. Six thousand dollars for Robert Morris. Six thousand men fed and paid.

"Thank God," he told McCrae.

"There's nothing to be thankful for," McCrae said dourly, as they walked back to Front Street. "I've bought eight thousand dollars' worth of goods, and we haven't a thousand dollars with which to pay for it."

"Something will turn up," Salomon said.

"Will it? And suppose nothing turns up and we're ruined? And suppose for all your service you end in a debtors' prison?"

"Something will turn up," Salomon said calmly.

But underneath he felt no such calm. He tried hard to smile across the dinner table at Rachel that night, yet found it an almost impossible task.

"Won't you give yourself any peace ever?" she pleaded, seeing the worry in his dark eyes.

"Yes, soon. Soon, Rachel, this will all be over. We'll sit back then. We'll find a little place in the country—a peaceful place."

"Will we—really?"

"Soon."

"But how long? Cornwallis surrendered. Doesn't that mean the war will be over soon?"

"When they sign a peace treaty," Salomon said. "And we may receive news from Europe that they've signed any day now."

"I'm glad," she said.

But in his heart he knew it would not be soon, that long years would pass before the war was really over.

His buying did not break him. News of De Grasse's defeat came, and people realized that the British blockade was still in force. He was able to sell for better than his buying price, and for a short time Mr. McCrae had the sense of being in charge of a wealthy firm.

Yet the money did not last. There were too many hands reaching out.

CHAPTER TWENTY-THREE

YET there were times when Haym Salomon felt he was being rewarded as fully as any man could desire. As, for instance, the time when the captured colors of Cornwallis passed through Philadelphia.

These battle flags belonged to the British, Scotch, Irish, and German regiments which had comprised Cornwallis's army. In slow stages they were brought up from Virginia. As they passed through each town and village and hamlet, a guard of honor came out to escort them some of the distance.

There were no uproarious demonstrations this time, such as had been seen when news of the surrender came. The first heat of victory had died away, and now it was with almost somber wonder that the people regarded the battle standards of a world-famous army, now in the hands of tattered, backwoods Continentals.

197

At last the flags came to Philadelphia, where their final resting place would be. A troop of the Philadelphia Light Horse went out to meet them, and with slow, measured tread, the flags came into the city.

The procession passed down Market Street to Front Street, and there, standing in front of his house, Haym Salomon saw the captured trophies move past him, so close that he could almost reach out and touch them.

He followed the standards slowly and thoughtfully, one of the crowd, yet one apart from them. He had believed, and now it had come to pass.

The procession wound through Chestnut Street, and then the flags were deposited in Independence Hall. Haym Salomon listened to speeches, the words of which he did not hear. Instead, he heard the suffering cries of thousands of persecuted men and women.

"They will no longer be without refuge," he told himself.

Now a scheme was afoot, an old and pet scheme of Robert Morris's, to create a National Bank of North America. He believed that such a bank would cure some of the nation's financial distress, but it would require money.

Somehow he squeezed the aching Treasury for capital, but it was not enough. He turned to his friends, Haym Salomon among them. Salomon found nine hundred dollars of his own for the bank, and among friends who trusted him he raised almost seven thousand dollars more. The bank was on its way.

198

Another step had been covered in the struggle to keep bankruptcy from the infant republic.

Yet while the bank was necessary and covered a gap left in the future, it did not provide for the present. There was still fighting in the South. They needed horses, ammunition, food, clothes. And at Newburgh General Washington had an army to feed.

The requests poured in, but the Treasury was dry. The winter promised to be a cold one. Robert Morris racked his brain, and as always, when everything else had failed, called for Haym Salomon.

"We must have money!"

Salomon never rested now. He had lost all track of where money went. He knew only that it wasn't enough. He sold bills of exchange by threatening, exhorting, pleading, bullying. And after the bills were sold, there was still a woeful shortage.

Desperately, in order to fill the gap, Robert Morris resorted to everything and anything. If the government had a hundred hides in its warehouse, he would call Salomon and say:

"Sell them, sell them."

And Salomon would go to the market and bully and plead for shillings and pennies. And a few precious dollars would come in.

"Turn the money over," Morris would beg him. "Find a rising market."

In its last extremities, the Treasury had become a trader, competing against the other traders of the coffee-

199

house. Haym Salomon bought anything that might be sold for a profit. Even the canny Mr. McCrae became lost in the maze of accounts.

The two of them, the small, thin Jew and the tall, loose-jointed Scotsman, stalked among the piles of merchandise that littered the docks. They bought tobacco and shipped it to another section of the country where it might command a better price. They sold iron and bought copper. They sold copper and bought wool.

They prowled from warehouse to warehouse. They stormed and begged and cajoled men into selling, and they threatened and bullied men into buying.

And in the evening, there would be a few dollars' profit to show to the Superintendent of Finance. And whatever there was, ten dollars or a hundred dollars, he seized it eagerly, repeating the refrain:

"But it's not enough, not enough."

Robert Morris racked his brain and formed scheme after scheme. And Haym Salomon bought and sold.

He could no longer gather much money at the synagogue. He had drained the Jews dry. Often he wished that there were more Jews in the country, but from Maine to Florida there were less than three thousand of them.

Already almost one Jew in every five was under arms. In proportion to their number, they had contributed more men to the revolution than any other group in the country. And those who were left, too old or too weak to fight, had already felt the aching hand of Haym Salomon.

He could not raise much more money from them. In his endless search, he turned to every possibility. It made no difference how many times he was rebuffed, insulted, spurned.

If a dollar was to be found, a dollar that might buy food, then that was enough.

Somehow the year wound to its weary close. A cold winter had settled down, and the armies were hedged in by snow and ice. Still there was no change in the financial situation. Congress could not tax the people, and the cost of the war was mounting up into millions of dollars.

Salomon worked on in the coffeehouse. With winter closing down, his cough grew worse, yet he managed to keep going from day to day. Eying him from across the table, Mr. McCrae would shake his head worriedly.

The stream of pensioners who depended upon Salomon increased. Now that so much of the active campaigning was over, soldiers began drifting into Philadelphia, wounded men, men with an arm or leg missing, sick men, men whose discharge had not left them enough money to return to their homes and who were making the stopover at Philadelphia.

Some instinct, some whispered rumor, told them that one in the coffeehouse would help them, and to the coffeehouse they beat a path. They were never refused.

It made Salomon's heart ache to see how little the government could provide for those who had served her. He gave and gave, and if it meant stinting at home, Rachel did not complain.

"I have you," she would tell him cheerfully.

He was becoming more successful now at hiding his increasing illness. He sensed when a fit of coughing would come on, and he slunk away where no one could see the blood well up to his lips.

Once, when the pain was almost more than he could bear, he visited the doctor again.

"You're a headstrong man, Mr. Salomon," the doctor told him.

"I can't leave my work."

The doctor shrugged his shoulders.

There was another child now, three already. He could almost forget everything when he came home at night now, played with the children, watched them tugging at the dour Mr. McCrae's mustache.

At dinner, he tried to be as gay as possible. He drew energy from a store that he would soon burn up, and he seemed to realize that. He was wonderfully tender toward Rachel, and he never tired of planning with her for after the war.

"You'll have to get yourself a wife," he told Mr. McCrae. "We'll find ourselves some place in the country where there's sunshine and fresh air."

"Where the Treasury cannot find us," Mr. McCrae said unsmilingly.

"You'll miss your musty old coffeehouse," Rachel said.

"No—no," Salomon smiled. "It will be different then."

"God grant the war is over soon," Rachel said.

202

One night Rachel had a few of the elders of the synagogue to dinner. They spoke of one thing and another, and then one said:

"Soon the war will be over, Salomon. The men will be coming home. It seems to me that now is the time to build a real synagogue of our own for Philadelphia—instead of the hired hall where we have been worshiping. We will need more space. And it's a shame that when there are synagogues in so many other cities in America, Philadelphia should be without one."

"That's true," Haym Salomon agreed.

"You don't seem too happy over the prospect?"

"I wonder," Salomon said slowly. "There's so little money. And every penny is needed."

"Is there any need greater than a place for men to gather and to pray?"

"I know—but this is a bad time. They're pleading for money on every hand."

"Yet a cause like this."

They talked down Salomon's opposition. He could never forget the debt he owed to the Jewish community, stemming from that first day in Philadelphia when he had come to them empty-handed and they had received him.

Finally he consented to the construction of a synagogue, and pledged himself for one quarter of the cost. He didn't have the money, nor did he know from where the money would come.

Yet he had faith that something would turn up, and it

did. A ship in which he owned some shares ran through the blockade, and the synagogue was paid for.

At this time there came up a curious incident concerning the British prisoners made at the Yorktown surrender. These men, of whom there were many thousands, were quartered in various towns in Virginia and Pennsylvania. To the already overburdened government was given the task of feeding and quartering these men. Naturally, with all the requests their own army made, the government could do little.

The officers of certain of these troops, quartered at Lancaster, had bills of exchange drawn on European banks. No one would cash these bills, and in the meantime their men were slowly approaching certain starvation.

In the extremity of their need, they were advised to turn to a certain broker in Philadelphia, a man whose name was Haym Salomon.

At first Salomon hesitated. There were enough of his own government's bills to dispose of without raising money for the enemy. Then he recalled what he had suffered in the British jail of New York. English prisoners were well treated by the Americans, and he wondered whether the justness in dealing with all men of all kinds was not a mark of a country's worth.

These men had fought well and bravely for something they believed in. Was it right that they should starve now simply because they were prisoners?

He wrote to Lancaster:

*And draw on me for any sum by post or express,
it shall be honored at Sight, let the Amount be ever
so Great. The Bills may be drawn on New York or
London, if they are endorsed by their Commanding
Officer.*

Yours,

HAYM SALOMON.

So now, in addition to other burdens, he had that of feeding British prisoners.

For all that the money had been taken at a time like this, Salomon felt a great happiness in the fact that the Jews were building their own synagogue. It gave an air of permanence to their being in America, and he prayed devoutly that from this land they would wander no more.

With all his work, he still found time to talk with builders and carpenters, to go over plans, to give his expert opinion on the price of materials.

They decided that the building would be of red brick, simple in design, two stories high, with stained-glass windows facing east, in the direction of the long lost land of Zion. Yet for all that, it seemed to Haym Salomon that Zion lay west of them, in the unexplored miles of forested hills and valleys that was America.

A lot was purchased on Cherry Street, and work went ahead. It was finished and dedicated, the first synagogue to be erected in the city of Philadelphia.

CHAPTER TWENTY-FOUR

General von STEUBEN

THE game went on, but without any of the surcease
Haym Salomon had hoped for. The peace treaty
was as far off as ever, and in odd corners of the
states armed men still fought the revolution. But as one
point of resistance after another was put down, the battalions and regiments and legions marched toward Philadelphia, to receive orders from Congress as to whether
or not they should disband.

You must remember that in the time of the American
revolution, there was no national army. In the course of
the war years, a start had been made, but even the two
best-organized forces under the Continental command,
the Pennsylvania line and the New Jersey line, were state
forces, not national forces.

In addition to these, there were over a hundred bands

206

of men, ranging from the old Minute Men of 1775 to Morgan's Riflemen, a well-organized force of Virginia backwoodsmen. Every state officially raised regiments, and as these regiments went to pieces with losses and desertions, new regiments were formed. Also private individuals, if the mood so took them, raised little armies of their own. Clubs and associations got together and organized themselves into militia.

There was a looseness to this sort of organization. Men disgusted with the war packed up and went home. Some regiments were ill trained, and some were not trained at all.

But now the war had been going on for seven years. What regiments remained were composed mostly of veterans. And their leaders had fat account books of money paid out, salaries for months in arrears, costs for this and costs for that.

So when they came to Philadelphia, they desired not only to know whether the war was over as far as they were concerned, but also whether they would be paid for all the debts they had accumulated.

Congress knew well enough that the war was not over, that even with its victories, the thin fringe of thirteen states was far inferior to the might and strength of the British Empire. Until a peace treaty was signed, they desired that most of the regiments be kept under arms and ready for action.

"Very well," the commanders agreed. "But pay us."

There was no money to pay them, and Congress took the convenient way of sending them to Robert Morris.

207

And the harassed Superintendent of Finance took the even more convenient way of sending them on to Haym Salomon.

Somehow Salomon found the money. It was the old, old story, yet each time the problem was new and just as impossible. Yet he found the money.

The records show that he paid out some $830 to Armand's Legion, $276 to Karens' Regiment, $1,481 to Vanheer's Corps.

The machine had to function.

Robert Morris drove him. The little man looked paler and weaker than ever as he sat behind his table in the coffeehouse. He had been there for years now. Armies moved and men fought, but his own battle was a steady, grueling grind—with no rewards, no glory.

His hair was turning gray; his cheeks had fallen in, and fine lines had etched themselves all over his face.

"Enter seven hundred dollars for Mr. Smith," he would say to McCrae. Or, "Twelve hundred dollars for Mr. Loring."

Morris gave him no peace. The calls for him to attend the office of finance increased. Morris would be sitting there with some officer, some general, perhaps George Washington himself. Yet they would hardly notice the little retiring Jew as he entered the room.

"We need five thousand dollars immediately, Mr. Salomon," Morris would say.

The officer would look at the little Jew, and then, an hour later, would forget that he had ever seen him.

Thus it went on, day after day, the calls to Morris's office; day after day, the demands for money. As Robert Morris wrote it down in his diary, it reads with strange monotony:

I sent for Mr. Salomon.
I sent for Haym Salomon.
I sent for Salomon.
I sent for Mr. Salomon.

A man he could always send for. Perhaps it would be the Marquis de Lafayette sitting in white and golden elegance and glancing curiously at the little man, who had almost nothing to say, only receiving his orders and carrying them out.

One or two remembered him. Baron von Steuben, for instance. It did the baron's heart good to see Salomon, to know that here was one with whom he could chatter easily in his own language instead of blundering through this barbarous tongue called English.

The baron was a frequent visitor at the Treasury office. As you remember, he had arrived in America years before, in time to give new life to the freezing men at Valley Forge. He had drilled them into shape, fined them down into an army.

But now the fighting was for the most part over. He had been made inspector general of the army, and in the work of keeping the armed forces together, it was his place to inspect. But how could he inspect when his uniform was dirty, patched cloth, when he hadn't even the money for one of those wonderful Cuban cigars he loved so much, when he couldn't feed his orderlies or his staff, all of whom had gone without pay for months?

Morris was glad enough to have Salomon there to relieve him of the baron's guttural complaints. And Salomon could always find money to tide him along.

Sometimes there would be a run on the bills, and a panic would seize the men who held them. This was what Salomon dreaded most of all. For to sell the bills and to have a market for them, he had to make sure that the value of these bills of exchange were never doubted.

Since they were drawn upon French banks, almost anything was likely to happen. A rumor would cross the ocean that some French bank had failed, and then holders of the bills would be clamoring at his door for him to back up his endorsement.

Once this happened with a set of bills drawn on Monseur Boutin, Treasurer of the Marine Department of France. McCrae acquainted him with the news late one evening.

"I've met Varis," McCrae said. "He's told me there's a rumor spreading that your Boutin bills are no good."

"They're good," Salomon said.

"Yes, but if you refuse to pick them up and refund money, it will break the market for a month."

"Then I'll pick them up," Salomon said calmly.

"How? We haven't a thousand dollars cash."

"I don't know how. But I'll do it—" He couldn't stop to think. If he had ever given his doubts a chance, they would have overwhelmed him. He wrote the following advertisement, and gave it to McCrae to have printed in the morning papers:

HAYM SALOMON

Takes this method to acquaint all those who possess full Sets of Bills of Exchange, drawn in his favor and endorsed by him on Monsieur Boutin, Treasurer of the Marine Department of France, that they shall, on application, have the money refunded; and for bills of the above description which may have already been sent to France, satisfactory assurance will be given to the proprietors that they shall be paid, agreeable to their relative tenors, in Paris, April 19.

"That will hold them," he told McCrae.

"But it won't keep us from bankruptcy."

"No—but I'll get the money somehow."

He went out that night, from friend to friend, begging, pleading. For himself, he would have starved before he dunned for a penny. But this was for his cause.

Late that night, he came home with enough money to cover the first day's run, but he was worn and aching. He wondered whether he would be able to endure another year of this.

The calls from Morris went on. Day after day he took his way to the Treasury office and back. Morris no longer put any task beyond his powers.

Luzerne was the one who suggested that he might seek some official position for himself. One day, Luzerne dropped into the coffeehouse, sat in Salomon's booth, and said:

"It's some time since we've spoken, my friend. Shall we have a cup of coffee together?"

"I am honored," Salomon nodded.

He poured the coffee. Luzerne was watching him quizzically.

"You seem older, my little friend," Luzerne said.

"Older, but not much wiser."

"I like your sense of humor. They say that you are a very sick man, yet you are always here at your place."

"My place is a small one," Salomon answered. "It's little enough that I do."

"Is it? I think that if others had done so much, this war might have been over years ago."

"I sometimes wonder whether all of this is worth anything," Salomon mused.

"Do you? My friend, you are worth to your country— how shall I say?—a regiment. No, more than that. The hardest way to work is underground, where no one sees and no one hears. Once the peace is signed, with all the shouting and all the trumpets blown, who will think of a little broker?"

"It doesn't matter," Haym Salomon said.

"But it does. Look, there are too many less worthy men filling long-sounding positions. If I were you, I would seek such a position for myself."

"I don't want that," Salomon said.

212

"You owe it to yourself and to your people."

So it came about that Haym Salomon humbly asked Robert Morris whether he might not style himself as "Broker to the Office of Finance." Morris agreed; indeed, it was the very least that he could do for Haym Salomon.

Salomon wrote the following advertisement for the *Freeman's Journal:*

HAYM SALOMON

BROKER TO THE OFFICE OF FINANCE, TO THE CON-
SUL GENERAL OF FRANCE AND TO THE TREASURER OF
THE FRENCH ARMY.

At his office in Front Street between Market and Arch Streets.

Buys and Sells on Commission, Bank Stock, Bills of Exchange on France, Spain, Holland and other parts of Europe, the West Indies and Inland Bills, at the usual Commissions. He buys and sells Loan Office Certificates, Continental and State Money of this or any other State, paymaster and quartermaster general's notes; these and every other kind of paper transactions (bills of exchange excepted) he will charge his employers no more than one half of one per cent for his commission.

He procures Money on Loan for a short time and gets notes and bills discounted.

Gentlemen and others residing in this State or in any of the United States, by sending their orders to the office, may depend on having their business transacted with as much fidelity and expedition as if they were themselves present.

He receives tobacco, sugars, tea and every other sort of goods to sell on commission for which purpose he has provided proper stores.

He flatters himself that his assiduity, punctuality and extensive connections in his business as a broker is well established in various parts of Europe and in the United States in particular.

All persons who shall please to favor him with their business may depend upon his utmost exertion for their interest and part of the money advanced if desired.

This advertisement was the one bit of vainglory he allowed himself. When it was printed, he showed it to Rachel.

"It's wonderful," she said. "It's strange how I never dreamed that there would be anything like this for us that night in New York—when they came to take you away."

"I've been very lucky," he said. "And very happy, Rachel. I'll never forget how happy I was with you."

"You always will be."

CHAPTER TWENTY-FIVE

PEACE was approaching. There were no doubts about it now; signs showed on every hand. The British blockade was slackening off, fighting had almost died out. And now the legislators and statesmen were turning their minds toward what sort of nation would face the prospect of peace—after such a long and ruinous war.

But at the Treasury building and at the coffeehouse, the little group of financiers still fought their silent struggle with unabated ferocity. Even the prospect of peace was bringing to a climax the long-accumulated war debts. Philadelphia had become an almost worldly metropolis, but it was filled with the poor, the hungry, the demanding, the deserving, and the undeserving.

215

War profiteers, speculators, traders, and some merchants had money. Apparently no one else did.

That went for the members of Congress. The government of the confederation was supposed to pay them some sort of salary, but it was amazingly small, and a good part of it was cheerfully offered in worthless Continental dollars. As one member of Congress said, "The stuff does not even burn well."

The states they represented were supposed to pay their expenses, but the states were a long way from Philadelphia. And the states had other problems which they considered far more important. Let the Congressmen shift for themselves.

Haym Salomon, the harassed little man of the coffee-house, found another problem added to the hundred and one he had already assumed. He realized that the battle would shift from the army to Congress, and he knew that a half-starved, half-clothed Congressman cannot perform his functions very well.

He gave the money as delicately as he could, yet often it was a difficult business, as in the case of James Madison, the young delegate from Virginia. The United States, as they exist now, were still unknown then, and certainly no one concerned foresaw that the blue-eyed young Madison would some day be President of the United States.

But nonetheless he was necessary, just as each of the Congress was necessary for the difficult period that was approaching. He, along with others, was dirt poor. His

poverty embarrassed him, harassed him, and sometimes made him weak with hunger. For all that he was in close contact with Robert Morris, he could not bring himself to make demands upon the Treasury.

For one thing, his pride forbade that, and for another, he saw at firsthand the long stream of the hungry and the poor whom Morris had to turn away.

A friend told him, "See Haym Salomon, the little Jew at the coffeehouse."

His pride rebelled against that too. For one thing, he didn't like Jews. He had hardly known one Jew in all his lifetime, but from what he had read, they were a heartless race with no other thought than to bleed poor debtors.

However, pride is one thing and poverty is another. He took the path to the coffeehouse. He asked for Haym Salomon, and there was pointed out to him a mild little man with strangely gentle brown eyes. When Madison approached, Salomon courteously invited him to sit down, pouring him coffee and inviting him to drink.

Somehow Madison blundered out his purpose in coming there. But Salomon cut him short.

"Please—only tell me how much you need."

Madison mentioned a figure, and Salomon nodded at McCrae, who counted out the money and gave it to Madison.

He took the money, trying to reconcile this with all the stories he had heard of how Jews do business. Then he remembered interest charges and stories he had heard of usury.

217

"What will the interest be?" he demanded cannily.

"Interest?" Salomon shook his head. "I didn't speak of interest. The money is yours. Whenever you can, you will pay me back. That is all."

"But all moneylenders charge interest," Madison said stubbornly.

"I'm not a moneylender," Salomon replied, in a tone that terminated the conversation.

But being forced to go to a Jew, even though this little man was not like any Jew he had ever heard of, still annoyed Madison. He wrote to a Virginia friend:

I cannot in any way make you more sensible to the importance of your kind attention to pecuniary remittances for me than by informing you that I have for some time been a pensioner on the favor of Haym Salomon, a Jew broker.

But Madison's attitude did not last long. He realized soon enough that he was not the only member of Congress who treaded the path to the coffeehouse to receive the open-handed bounty of the little man. Whosoever was in need came to Haym Salomon.

And he gave freely and generously, requiring no note and no interest. The list of his pensioners reads like a register of our early history.

There was Thomas Mifflin, to be governor of Pennsylvania; John Reed, member of Congress; Edmund Randolph, aide to Washington, member of Congress; Arthur

218

Lee, member of Congress; Arthur St. Clair, veteran soldier; James Monroe, to be twice President of the United States and author of the famous Monroe Doctrine.

There were Steuben, Kosciusko, Mercer, Wilson, Jones . . .

For all that he gave, in most part, his confidence was not misplaced, and most of the loans were repaid.

It was not long before Madison wrote to the same friend:

> The kindness of our little friend in Front Street near the Coffee House, is a fund that will prevent me from extremities, but I never resort to it without great mortification, as he obstinately rejects all recompense. The price of money is so usurious that he thinks it ought to be extracted from none but those that aim at a profitable speculation. To a necessitous delegate he gratuitously spares a supply out of his private stock.

McCrae warned Salomon, "How long can you go on giving money to every beggar who comes asking?"

"Beggars? I was a beggar once myself, Mr. McCrae."

It was a long, hard winter. People were suffering in Philadelphia. Food was scarce. Soldiers returning from the war added to the list of the homeless and foodless.

Haym Salomon gave money quietly and easily. When his money ran low, he sold real estate and other property he had accumulated. He had no doubts as to his own ability to earn more money. Bread cast on water would always return to the giver.

And meanwhile, so long as he should be able to help, no one who had fought and suffered for his country would go hungry.

Anyone and everyone found the way to the coffee-house. Even Don Francisco Rendon, Royal Emissary from his most Christian Majesty, the King of Spain.

The King of Spain was keenly interested in the outcome of the war. While he did not dare to help the states outright, as France had done, he prayed that they would break Britain's might, and he sent his personal emissary, Rendon, to spur them on and report to him.

The emissary arrived at Philadelphia, but his funds somehow went astray, and he was soon sorely put upon to keep up his dignity as representative of the Spanish King. However, they told him:

"If your need is necessary to our cause, then go to the coffeehouse on Front Street."

He went there, and Haym Salomon found himself with a Spanish Don on his bounty.

"It will be a king next time," McCrae grinned. "Unless we are beggars first."

"Unless we are beggars first," Haym Salomon thought.

Even patient Rachel would sometimes complain about their circumstances.

"No, it will soon be over," Salomon assured her. "I

220

can see signs of the end now. If we hold on for only a little while longer—"

"Will you rest then?" she asked him. "Will we really have that house in the country you speak of?"

"All of it," he smiled, kissing her.

"Sometimes you remember that I'm your wife," she admitted.

"I always remember it."

"You make me so afraid. You're not well. Don't you ever think of your wife and family? If something happened—"

"Nothing will happen," he reassured her.

Yet his work increased and his health grew worse. There were the ever-present bills of exchange, the endless task of raising money. And there was also the task of finding money for himself, for his charities, for his pensioners.

The British blockade was relaxing. As word was passed from vessel to vessel on the high seas, the British ship captains came to realize that for all purposes the war was finished.

These were boom times for Philadelphia. From bank to bank the Delaware River was crowded with ships, their masts like a wintry forest. Carpenters drove piles and built additional docks, and the mounds of merchandise grew to fantastic heights.

The thirteen states were shaking loose from an eight-year blockade. From Maine to Florida, from the coast to the mountains, the people of the states were demanding all the multitude of things that had been denied them during the war.

They wanted tea, cotton, linen, iron, flour, lead, glass, wool, spices—they wanted all the varied products that pour into a country at peace.

Prices were soaring, dropping, soaring again, dropping again, fluctuating always. What with all his other work, Haym Salomon still had to be down at the docks. He had to buy and sell, buy and sell. Money had to be earned, for no matter how much he earned, it drained away like water flowing down a spout.

The doctor had warned him again, and it frightened him to think of leaving Rachel and the children nothing for all his years of work. Yet he lacked all ability to refuse. When someone asked, he gave, and that was all there was to it.

He worked furiously, from early dawn until darkness. It even wore out the long-limbed Mr. McCrae, who followed him around always with the battered old account book.

He bought and sold. A hundred bales of cotton, fifty barrels of flour, two hundred bales of linen. He sensed when prices would rise and when they would fall. The money poured in, yet somehow, as much of it as came in, more than that was paid out.

He would remark wistfully to Mr. McCrae, "How does a man become rich? Day after day our books show a profit, yet at the end of the month I am always a little deeper in debt."

222

It was the last day of March, the year was 1783. Winter had passed, and the first signs of a glorious spring were beginning to appear. Philadelphia was alive with progress, with activity, with rumor.

And then, just before midday, with sails spread, the ship *Triomphe* sailed slowly up the Delaware. At first, while she was still in the distance, she was given hardly more than the passing attention any new ship in that busy port deserved.

Then the men on the docks heard her bells ringing and saw that her rails swarmed with yelling, screaming sailors. Other sailors climbed the masts and hung from the tops.

Boats put out, and the *Triomphe* nosed into shore.

"What is it?" everyone demanded. "What is it?"

Then the news ran from person to person. "The war is over!" "There's been a peace treaty signed at Paris!"

"For good, this time!"

"The war's over!"

"The men will be coming home now!"

"We've won the war—and it's over!"

"The war is over!"

All over the city bells began to clang. Boys, screaming the news, ran helter-skelter through the streets. Staid, sober citizens of Philadelphia danced in the streets. Discharged Continental soldiers wiped the tears out of their eyes and looked uneasily into an uncertain future.

Officers met and embraced. Members of Congress danced like children and clapped their hands.

223

A great crowd gathered in front of Independence Hall as the old Liberty Bell began to send forth its ringing tones.

"There must be a parade," someone said.

And men ran home for their militia uniforms, so that they could march in the parade.

In the coffeehouse someone ran in with the news. And there the celebration was continued. All trading stopped. The landlord opened a dozen bottles of his best rum and invited everyone and anyone to come forward and drink on the house.

Haym Salomon sat rigid, staring at Mr. McCrae. "Do you hear?" he asked.

"The war's over," McCrae nodded.

"Over—and we've won."

"We've won," McCrae nodded.

"Thank God," Salomon said.

They pressed around his table. "Drink with us, Salomon!" they cried.

"We all drink," the landlord smiled.

"You too, McCrae. Have a drink with us, Salomon!" they insisted.

"Yes, I'll drink with you."

They poured the rum, and the little man rose slowly and held out the glass. He looked very old, very tired, but there was such a gleam of triumph in his eyes as no one could fail to note.

They gathered around him in a circle. Instinctively, they seemed to realize what his service had been, and they paid him the silent tribute of waiting for him to make the toast.

"Gentlemen," he said, raising his glass, "to the United States of America—"

They drank.

He said to McCrae, "I'll go home now. I want to be with Rachel."

CHAPTER TWENTY-SIX

THEY held a celebration for the war's end. There was a great gathering at the long walnut table in Haym Salomon's dining room. The two oldest children were allowed to remain awake, and they listened in dazzled wonder to all the talk of what would be now that the revolution had ended.

Old friends were there, a Congressman, officers, elders from the synagogue, wind-weathered sea captains, traders. Even the dour Mr. McCrae relaxed for once and drank more wine than was good for him. They all spoke of the future, of all the great opportunities that would now open up in the land.

Only now and then, when such talk ran high, Rachel noticed a trace of sadness in Haym Salomon's eyes, as if he were not at all certain of what that future would be.

The next day word came from the office of Robert

226

Morris that he would like to see Haym Salomon. And Haym Salomon went.

"You see," Robert Morris explained, "with us, things haven't changed—not yet. I hope for the best. I hope that Congress will come out of its stupor, find a way to levy taxes. Money must be raised, and we can't go on forever selling bills of exchange. For one thing, France won't continue the loans. For another, this war has left us with a debt of millions of dollars."

"The only answer to that," Salomon said, "is a sound currency."

"And with God's help, we will do so. But meanwhile, Congress has voted half pay to officers. Regiments will be disbanded. The men will be coming home, and who knows how many thousands of them will stop at Philadelphia to collect their back pay? We must have money, more now than ever before, if we are to come out of this war with any sort of financial stability."

"I see," Salomon nodded.

"And that means you must find a market for bills of exchange. I have certain bills here—"

So it went. While the shouting and applause still lingered, Haym Salomon was back in his place in the coffeehouse, still dragging the reins of an almost bankrupt nation, still hoarsely demanding money and more money.

Days passed into weeks and weeks into months. Haym Salomon's health grew worse, his eyes more weary. And Mr. McCrae's face came to have a hunted look as he thumbed over the pages of his ancient ledger.

"Only a little while longer," Haym would tell Rachel.

"And how long must I hear that same thing?" she would say tiredly.

"Not for long, my little wife."

"But for years it was always, 'just a little longer'—or 'when the war is over.' But now the war *is* over."

"I know. But they need me."

"And how long will they need you?"

Haym Salomon would shake his head and try to laugh away her doubts.

The troops were mustered out. A tall, weary, sad-eyed man had stood in Annapolis some months past and resigned his commission as commander in chief of the Continental army.

Standing there, George Washington said very simply:

"Having now finished the work assigned me, I retire from the great theater of action; and, bidding farewell to this august body, under whose orders I have so long acted, I here offer my commission and take my leave of all the employments of public life."

He was speaking to the Congress, to the poor harassed Congress which had somehow muddled through eight years of war.

So he went on his way, back to the broad acres of the old home at Mount Vernon, and others went on their way, having each played his part, well or poorly.

The troops marched home, here and there a man alone,

his first trip, but he said it would be better if she remained with the children.

However, he assured her that he would be back within a few weeks.

They set about making things ready, and in a short time Haym Salomon was ready to leave. He felt like a boy again at this, his first vacation in so many years.

So when at last he sat on the stage in the bright spring sunshine, the eager horses champing at the road, Rachel and McCrae waving at him, his heart felt lighter than it had in many years.

CHAPTER TWENTY-SEVEN

IT WAS only a little more than a year ago that the British had given up New York and General Washington had reoccupied the city, but already it was making great headway as a center of commerce, fast overtaking Philadelphia.

Shipmen found it far easier to sail into the broad, placid harbor of New York than to make their arduous way up the Delaware River to Philadelphia. Also New York was situated about as well as a city might be in America, dead center between the New England and the southern states.

So in spite of the long British occupation, New York was already a booming postwar city. Most of the Tories had gone with the British, and those merchants and journeymen who had fought with the American army

234

had come home. They were rebuilding the houses that had burned in the two great fires during the British occupation, and New York was alive with prosperity.

Perhaps Haym Salomon sensed some of the future that was in store for New York when he decided to make a trip there.

It was in strange contrast to his previous journey, when he had walked all the distance and come into Philadelphia a penniless stranger. This time he rode by stage, and although the trip took three days, it was still an improvement over walking. To the people of the day, the heavy stagecoach, lurching along the rutted road, bounding and rocking, was still the best-known form of transportation.

For all that, the trip was hard on him. He was not very strong, and the dust and lurching brought back his cough. However, he determined to ignore the pain in his chest, to ignore anything that might interfere with the pleasure of riding as a free man in a free country.

He was smiling happily when at last the ferry from Staten Island landed him at the Battery.

He walked slowly through the streets of the old city, picking out a landmark here and a landmark there, seeing many new faces and a few old ones.

It was strange how he would brush against someone, how that person would turn and stare at him, and how they would then be shaking hands.

"Salomon!"

"Langdon!"

It would be one of the now ancient Sons of Liberty,

and there was nothing else to it but that they must go to
the nearest tavern and compare fortunes over a glass of
hot rum.

And then a tale would be told on both sides, and he
would hear one more story to fit into his picture of the
American revolution, as it had been.

Or it would be some fat merchant who had winked his
way all through the British occupation, selling them this
and that and waiting for the day when they would be
gone.

"I never thought to see you in the flesh. They had you
in the Provost that night for hanging."

Or a storekeeper whose shop he entered again.

Or a businessman who had heard of the little broker
of the coffeehouse.

He took a room at an inn, but he found it hard to rest.
Coming back here was like coming back into a dream. He
had to see each place, the path his escape had taken,
where he had hidden, where he had fled.

He hired a chaise one sunny morning and rode up
through the island to see Vanhelb. His arms were loaded
with gifts, one in particular being a fine suit of clothes
with which to repay that long-standing debt.

When he entered the farmhouse, the Vanhelbs scarcely
recognized him. And when they did, they were more than
ever astonished to realize that this stranger in the fine
dark coat was the same poor fugitive whom they had
given refuge.

When they tried to refuse his gifts, he showed that he
could be stubborn as well as mild, and finally they took

236

them. They persuaded him to stay on for dinner, and he had to tell them all of his adventures.

There was a strange nostalgia about being back in New York, and now that he was there, he had no real desire to return to Philadelphia. He was almost tempted to write to his family and tell them to come along and join him.

But then he realized that there were too many matters left unsettled in Pennsylvania, that he would have to go back and clear up his affairs.

He wondered whether it was given to a man to have such fortune, to work for his heart's desire, to achieve it, and then to be able to rest afterward. Sometimes he was shaken by an awful fear for the future.

Then he had a hemorrhage, and he lay in his room, gasping painfully for breath. A doctor came and examined him and then shook his head.

"You're a sick man," the doctor said. "A very sick man."

It was hard to lie alone like that. No one knew of his sickness, and he felt a strange reluctance to inform any of his friends in New York.

Three days later he left his bed against the doctor's warning. But it was a wonderful, golden day, and he could not lie in bed and watch the sun through his windows.

He went down to the Battery and sat there for hours, staring at the ships moored against the dock and at anchor in the harbor. Already the news had spread across the world that New York was a free port again, and from all lands the vessels had come, their sides fat with cargo, from Spain, from Holland, from France, from England, from the East Indies and from the West Indies, from Italy and from Greece.

Their long pennons flew in the wind, and high above them, from the tall flagstaff of the Battery, as to show them the way, flew that newest of all flags.

Haym Salomon gazed up at it, at the strange conglomeration of many colors, red and white and blue, and stars and stripes.

He remembered the other flags, the Rattlesnake Flag and the Pine Tree Flag and the flag they had raised at Cambridge in 1776, with the British colors backing up the stripes. It all seemed such a long time ago now.

He had met one Jacob Mordecai, a New York businessman, and they had discussed opening some sort of business in New York. Mordecai had had experience with the selling of goods of every type, as had Salomon, and finally they decided to open an auctioneering house, which would also serve as a sort of stock exchange.

Yet Salomon's attention wandered continually, and Mordecai wondered whether he had any real interest in the business. Even when they took an office on Wall Street and set it in order, Salomon did not appear too interested.

"You must forgive me," he told Mordecai, "but it's hard for me to plan for the future. I keep feeling that all the work I was needed for is done."

"We all have to plan for the future," Mordecai said stolidly.

"Yes, yes, of course. I beg your forgiveness."

But Salomon found that he was far more interested in lazy hours spent along the Battery than in the business. He would fall into conversation with old skippers, men who had been privateers and blockade runners. They would speak of mutual acquaintances, of how it had been in the old days when it depended upon the turn of a card whether or not a man could run the British blockade.

And in the end, sooner than he had expected, he decided to go back to Philadelphia. And for all that New York had taken him and captured him, he felt no regret at leaving it.

CHAPTER TWENTY-EIGHT

IT WAS good to come into the coffeehouse again, to sense the old, familiar acrid smell, to be greeted by old friends, old enemies. It was good to be able to walk down to the docks on the Delaware and see the piles of merchandise lying just as they had always lain.

It was good, even, to be back in Robert Morris's office, with the portly Superintendent of Finance smiling at him curiously.

To hear all the bustle and rush of Philadelphia.

He seemed almost disappointed as he told Rachel of the arrangements he had made to return to New York. She urged him to leave, for she was afraid that something or other would turn up to keep him there.

"Soon," he promised her.

He went back to his place in the coffeehouse, but there was little for him to do. Already the war was past and talk was all of the future, of prospects for commerce, of the new opening of the West.

240

And then he took sick again.

He promised Rachel solemnly, "As soon as I'm out of bed again, we'll leave. We'll find that little house I spoke of—somewhere on Manhattan."

"Yes," Rachel said tenderly, "as soon as you are well."

"And it won't be long," he smiled. "I really think the air is better for me in New York."

"Only rest."

The doctor told her, "I warned him of this—I warned him years ago, Mrs. Salomon."

Rachel almost never left his bedside. But there was little to hope for. His cheeks had fallen in and his hair was almost all gray. He was only forty-five, but already he looked like an old man.

The slow days and weeks crawled past, but this time he could not make a recovery. His store of hidden strength had been drained to the bottom, and now there was nothing left.

Once, when McCrae was by his bed, he motioned for the Scotsman to bend close.

"Take care of them, McCrae," he said. "There will be very little, very little for them."

And McCrae nodded and wiped the tears from his eyes.

The pain was going, and Haym Salomon dozed and dreamed a great deal now. Most often, he dreamed of his escape from New York, of his coming into the camp of the Continentals, of the ragged men and the ragged tents.

Sometimes, in his sleep, he heard their bugles again.

241

And again he heard the troops of General Washington marching through Philadelphia on their way to trap Cornwallis.

He died that way, peacefully, quietly, and the only sign that Rachel and McCrae had, watching by his bedside, was the sudden relaxing of all his strained features.

He was buried January 7, 1785, in the old Jewish burying ground. And around his grave, behind the weeping Rachel, half supported by Mr. McCrae, who for once had lost his stolidity, who cried without shame, stood hundreds of the Philadelphia people Haym Salomon had befriended.

Perhaps, standing there, they made for him an epitaph: "He gave without stint, and without putting shame in the hearts of those who asked."

SON OF LIBERTY

A HUNDRED AND FIFTY-SIX YEARS HAVE PASSED SINCE HAYM SALOMON WAS RECEIVED INTO THE GOOD EARTH OF THE COUNTRY HE MADE HIS OWN. THE OLD COFFEE-HOUSE IS GONE FROM FRONT STREET. BUT IF YOU WALK ALONG THERE, CLOSE YOUR EYES, LISTEN WITH AN EAR FOR WHAT IS PAST, YOU WILL RECAPTURE SOMETHING OF THE FRONT STREET THAT WAS HIS.

BREATHE DEEPLY OF THE COFFEE SMELL THAT STILL LINGERS IN THE AIR, OF THE ODOR OF FRAGRANT SPICES.

READ THE OLD BRONZE TABLETS THAT TELL OF THIS PLACE AND THAT PLACE.

GO DOWN THROUGH THE NARROW, SLOPING STREETS TO THE DELAWARE RIVER, AND YOU MAY STAND ON THE DOCKS, EVEN AS HAYM SALOMON DID.

AND THEN, GO TO SPRUCE STREET NEAR NINTH. THE OLD CEMETERY OF THE MIKVEH ISRAEL CONGREGATION IS STILL THERE, HIDING AWAY UNDER THE SHEER WALLS OF MODERN BUILDINGS.

BUT IF YOU GO THROUGH THE OLD IRON GATES AND TURN TO YOUR RIGHT, YOU WILL SEE A TABLET WHICH SAYS THAT SOMEWHERE WITHIN THE CONFINES OF THE OLD CEMETERY LIE THE REMAINS OF HAYM SALOMON, AMERICAN.

243